BIG EIGHT

Books by RICHARD G. HUBLER

Nonfiction

BIG EIGHT
SAC: THE STRATEGIC AIR COMMAND
IN DARKEST CHILDHOOD
FLYING LEATHERNECKS
LOU GEHRIG

Fiction

TRUE LOVE, TRUE LOVE
THE SHATTERING OF THE IMAGE
MAN IN THE SKY
THE BRASS GOD
I'VE GOT MINE
THE CHASE
THE QUIET KINGDOM
THE PASS

Others

ST. LOUIS WOMAN (with Helen Traubel)
I FLEW FOR CHINA (with Royal Leonard)

BIG EIGHT

A Biography of an Airplane

by
Richard G. Hubler

DUELL, SLOAN AND PEARCE

New York

Library of Congress Catalogue Card Number: 60-12830

MANUFACTURED IN THE UNITED STATES OF AMERICA

VAN REES PRESS • NEW YORK

TO JANE

ACKNOWLEDGMENTS

I SHOULD like to express my appreciation to Jim Edwards, A. E. Raymond, Bert Foulds, Carlos Wood, Ivar Shogran, Richard Davis, Stanley Lippert and John Roebuck, Ed Burton, Tom Toborg, Paul Patten, Bill Henry, Heimie Heimerdinger, Nat Paschall, R. L. Johnson, Eileen Porch, and others—especially the heads of twenty-one airlines and four manufacturing companies—for their interest and supply of data. United Air Lines has been unusually helpful.

In this book the term "Douglas" is used as a generic term. The founder and his company are so closely identified as to be virtually interchangeable. However, unless the specific meaning is otherwise, the word may be taken to refer to the company.

—R. G. H.

CONTENTS

ILLUSTRATIONS

following page 180

Donald W. Douglas, Sr., and Donald W. Douglas, Jr.

Donald W. Douglas, Sr., and United Air Lines' W. A. Patterson

E. V. Rickenbacker and Frank Boyer

The DC-8 taking off . . . in flight . . . landing

The DC-8

An Army Air Force C-47

A "Skymaster" Army C-54

The B-19

The B-66

An AD-5 Skyraider

An F4D Skyray

An A4D Skyhawk

The D-558-2 Skyrocket, first aircraft to exceed Mach 2

An X-3 high-speed research aircraft

Donald W. Douglas, Sr., on his first DC-8 ride

KLM, Alitalia, Trans-Canada Air Lines, Swissair, all fly DC-8's

BIG EIGHT

FROM SUB TO SUPER

1

THE DC-8 is probably the last great airplane. It is among the last of the pure-blooded, thoroughbred line that has brought man up from the surface of the earth so that he can stare unwinking into the black fringes of space. Not one man but thousands of men—millions of times—to spy into the unknown. Year by year the wings grow shorter and fade back as the evolution toward the stars takes place. What sleek, streamlined monsters will fling themselves upward in gouts of flame and claps of thunder in the days to come is no concern of the DC-8.

By that time she will have placidly fulfilled her mission. She will have retired to the pages of history to join her honored ancestors. Men will have known her intimately and grown to love her, and she will have been faithful to them in her fashion.

"You know what I said on that July day in 1933, the day the first DC-1 wobbled up off the runway?" says Donald Wills Douglas, the one man whose brain and will are responsible for the DC-8. "I said: 'She's up!' " He pauses and waits for his own words. "You know what I said twenty-five years later when the first DC-8 got into the sky? I said: 'She's up!' "

He spreads his fingers, as if he were letting go of something of value. "What else could I say?" he asks slowly.

It is his baby and he should know. It is too late now to turn back and re-enter the jungle of primitive aviation. The future is too bright, too close ahead—as if it were just beyond the fingertips, and a long run and a hell of a jump might make it easy.

2

The heart and guts, liver and lights of an airplane are easy to see. What cannot be seen is the soul of the symbol of this era, the ghost within the great hollow metal dart which has chastened time and flung man on his way to space.

If the heart is the crew and the guts are the power plant, what is left within the thin-skinned fuselage are the thousand components of experience, knowledge, and skill. Within the shining reality of aluminum alloy, these items are joined to fulfill the first stage of man's finest dream.

The principle that whatever the mind can imagine, man can do, was never so aptly illustrated as in the case of the airplane. The last specimens of this kind of air travel are already flying. In less than a generation, they may not amount to much more than scrap and memories, as has happened to planes before them. But in their lifetime they will have given their sponsors the incentive to rise literally above the environment of nature and reach toward the universe.

The DC-8 is the end product of the ingenuity of this sort of flight. It is the culminating creation of the most distinguished aircraft lineage in the world. Other carriers will rise into space after it is gone. Other, more sophisticated vehicles will take off toward the planets. The DC-8 has forecast its own fate: the days of the true "airplane" were finished when this giant dolphin of the atmosphere, with its swept-back finwings, became airborne May 30, 1958.

The DC-8 may be the finest expression of the plane that operates in the air. It is certainly the most refined result of the nearly sixty years of evolution of flight machines within the earth's ten-mile rind of atmosphere. The next step in evolution—sometime in the 1970's —will no longer be operational beneath the 617- to 760-mile-an-hour speed of sound. It will be supersonic, passing the barrier once thought to be the ultimate limit of speed. Nor will such carriers fly any longer in the troposphere, nine tenths of the earth's blanket of life. They will cruise, instead, at levels of more than fifteen miles above the surface, where piston engines lose all energy, where even ramjets must cram themselves to bursting with the thin stuff. They will be well into the second ring of space ether, the troposphere or the mesosphere, on vestigial wings.

Once these have appeared in flight, they will no longer be within the art of airplaning. They will not be true air breathers. As the Douglas experts point out, "The airplane, by definition, must always operate within the earth's atmosphere." Like the prehistoric creatures that crept out of the water and preferred to breathe in another element in our own dim history, such vehicles will have suffered a change that can only be revolutionary.

Those who ride in the cabin of the DC-8 ride with history, with the ending of a period that few may ever see again. In air travel, the future opens out too widely and swiftly for it to recoil on itself. Today the world, tomorrow the stars, is a motto to which all men in this flight-minded century must subscribe.

3

The DC-8 is a queer ship of heaven. On the ground, it looks trim but uncomfortable. It is ill at ease until it leaves the earth and seeks its own familiar regions. It does not agree with the traditional visions of other heavenly bodies, nor does it have any resemblance to a bird or beast. It is one of the purest examples of man's ingenuity and imagination, a concept out of the blue to which it returns. It flies in despite of the design of the bumblebee; it swims through the clouds like a fish. It carries freight and passengers, mail and baggage. It races the sun, and is content to lose in the knowledge that only a little more effort would send it beyond the leash of

nature that holds it to the old schedules of the sky. But it is not
built for bravado. It is merely a plane designed to do its humdrum,
peaceful errand as many times as possible, a plane designed to get
as many people as it can from one place to another within a range
of five thousand miles at its cruising speed of 575 miles-plus per
hour. It must do it time and time again, again and again, with
ultimate safety and comfort.

This is not a romantic or a glamorous mission. But the soul of
the DC-8, like that of a good husband, is dependent on what it
carries in its belly. It has been designed for a utilitarian life alone.
It must be judged on that basis.

4

The bold figure of the DC-8 does not stand by itself. No more
than any man can disavow the long line of ancestors that stretches
behind him, can the DC-8 disavow its legitimate descent. Its
mother, of course, may be traced back to the famous day in
December, 1903, at Kill Devil Hill at Kitty Hawk, North Carolina,
when the Wright brothers flew the first heavier-than-air machine.
The honorable genealogy of its father goes back no further than a
tiny biplane called the *Cloudster,* which got off the ground in 1921.

Since that time there have been seventy-eight legitimate major
descendants of the Douglas line. Three wars have accelerated the
tempo of production; forty years have accumulated a vast body
of knowledge. All of this has been combined into the DC-8, the
jet transport of the past two years. Its predecessor, the DC-7C,
was only a refined and enlarged version of the DC-6, which was
created in 1946. The DC-8 is virtually a full-blown creation of
special significance in its own right.

Yet each one of its ancestors has contributed in some way, however remote, to the final product. If the experiments that failed,
the scrapped blueprints, the bastard models that never reached
production are included, the begats that precede the DC-8 are
innumerable. Out of the Douglas roster of land and sea, sport and

fighter, cargo and passenger, bomber and reconnaissance—all of which are intimately related in three main bloodlines—came the cumulative concept. Everything on the DC-8 is derivative. And everything is new.

The DC-8 is the capstone of a pile of data and know-how that represents the most comprehensive body of airplane facts in the world. These deal not only with the plane itself but its environment, its past and projected future, its men and machines, its own unknown destiny.

This corpus of hard fact is important because it is the bridge over which man has passed from one phase to another of his life in the air. What is known about the abysmal heights and depths that surround his chosen refuge is, in large part, due to the scientists, researchers, and practical men who went ahead to a special rendezvous in which they could only believe. Men have died— violently and in their beds—for the DC series of planes. Such sacrifices for machines would seem a senseless worship of Moloch if it were not for the long look forward. Many more men have managed to live long enough to extend their perimeter of knowledge about the air and its mastery until at length there was enough in hoarded skills and insured strategy to get victory.

5

Like much of man's comprehension, aeronautical knowledge does not seem to correspond to a gradual rise on a graph. Historically, it appears more as if a spring were being compressed. At the end of a certain time it releases itself to jump forward. This length of time, called "the state of the art," is needed to accumulate enough tension in the form of correlated data. It can be estimated at eight to ten years.

Such an increment of understanding is not the only factor involved. For better or worse, the advances in the aviation latitudes must grow from what came before. If some vast wave of mnemonic destruction were to engulf men, their memories and records, the survivors would find themselves faced with the possibility of a new vision of man in the sky—but hardly a clue of how to get him there.

The very nature of man is of inestimable assistance in such advances. One man flies; another sees him and wants to imitate his feat. In that instant competition is born. In the construction of airplanes, as in all else, the continuing desire to surpass the next fellow is a deciding factor in progress.

6

The first problem of flight is to create a power plant sufficient to overcome gravity. The hummingbird does it one way, a way that man does not yet completely understand. The engine, from piston to jet to rocket, does it another.

The second poser that must be met is the building of the vehicle itself. The airframe must be light and powerful. But it must include in its design something that is close to a contradiction of these engineering goals: a safety factor of three to ten times over expected ordinary stresses.

Third, any plane must be so configured that, like the young man on the trapeze, it flies through the air with the greatest of ease. Last of all, powered and designed and configured, it must be a product that can be manufactured at a price and for a duration of service that will enable its owner to make money. A good airplane is an excellent example of the highest form of commercial idealism.

Even if all these objectives are successfully met, if all the strenuous tests of the company and the government are passed, if the plane itself meets the fancy of the public, the men who make it and the men who fly it can expect to lose a good deal of money over a measurable length of time. If their luck holds, after such an interval they may commence to recoup their losses.

7

The transition from the earth to the air is an unforgiving one. It has meant the re-education of man, in the sense that he has been persuaded to abandon his birthright of solid ground. It has meant accidents, idiocy, errors, and disaster in an area where any one such lesson is invariably tragic. "Trouble is our teacher," says one Douglas engineer. "Once in a while she cracks us across the knuckles so hard, you don't think you can stand it."

First and last, the development of the DC-8 has cost innumerable man-months of sweat, tears, fantasy, and occasionally blood; although the DC-8 itself, at this writing, has not been responsible for a single human death. The vision of the Victorian poet in Locksley Hall, who "saw the heavens fill with commerce," has been fulfilled more by Douglas than by any other human agency. Tennyson's "pilots of the purple twilight," and their freight and passengers, have come in DC's.

In round dollars, the ultimate product of the DC-8 rests upon an expenditure of more than $500,000,000. From this point, what is to come in commercial aviation opens out in two different directions: above and below what has been accomplished.

8

A plane like the DC-8 is, in one sense, self-defeating. It is designed for the long haul, for the many passengers, for the maximum in subsonic commercial transport. It cannot hope to compete, for example, in the multitudinous short hops such as are undertaken efficiently by the smaller DC-3's and similar planes.

The economic state of these puddle jumps is now outmoded. Faster, cheaper, and better carriers must be developed. Most people like to travel short distances rather than long ones; much freight travels in short consignments. This field has fostered a large group of small, prosperous airlines that have succeeded (often with government aid) in the face of the competition of the airline giants. This sector of air transport represents one of the most fertile and untouched service areas in the world, especially in undeveloped nations.

Douglas, like other companies, must turn its attention to creating planes to open up this prospect. An example of this possibility is a new jet engine that weighs 250 pounds and produces 1,000 horsepower, as against the old piston engines that used to weigh 1,250 pounds and give 500 horsepower. With such power plants on the way, the small, fast, economical cargo and passenger planes are wholly feasible—in a spectrum that descends all the way from the 5,000-mile DC-8 flights to the 50-mile jumps between country towns.

9

The vast unexplored that lies above the pinnacle of the DC-8 is largely an enigma. It is only now being probed by the tools of research. It can be bounded easily: it lies between the earth's atmosphere and outer space.

Such a challenge offers a broad field for speculations. It can be dimly outlined by a return to the basic, intensely practical principles of Douglas. A good way to put it succinctly is to quote J. B. Edwards, assistant to the vice-president of engineering: "The only thing that counts in commercial people-flying is tail fatigue."

What he means is that passengers get tired. Even in the age of jet travel, some nonstop flights may take as long as twelve to fifteen hours. Other flights, with only a stop or two, may take days. That is a long time to sit in a seat, to be confined in the cage of a fuselage, no matter how comfortable.

The solution is more speed—getting more people faster, in comfort and safety, to the place where they want to go. This travel is important in another respect: if people do not like and respect such planes in person, they will not trust their goods to them.

The answer to more speed apparently lies in more power. Such power exists at this moment in the pure-jet engine, the ramjet, and, finally, the rocket. No such engine break-throughs as had to be made from the piston engine to the jet are needed. The technology, materials, and know-how have been assembled on the same narrow plateau.

What is missing is the demand for such speed, and the fragile-seeming mounting for whatever engine is selected. Nevertheless, if the development of aviation in the past means anything, this demand will come inevitably. The manufacturers of planes must be ready to match it with their product. "When a thing becomes technically feasible," says Edwards, "it always comes about."

10

The next increment of flight is not to be a simple growth, such as it was from the DC-1 to the DC-8. It will be a jump, off into the unknown and uncharted. Flight in the atmosphere could be essayed in a series of tentative steps, like a child walking. Flight above the atmosphere must necessarily be an extrapolation of psychological and technical skills.

One of the major problems is that of cost. A realistic estimate of the money necessary to build a reliable commercial-transport supersonic plane comes to something between a billion and a billion and a half dollars.

Even this enormous cost is not a total obstacle. This is accepted as a normal hazard of the future. If all the vectors that move in the same direction are lined up, they push companies like Douglas irresistibly forward. In doing so, they present a realistic picture of the air vehicle of the future.

Like the United States Air Force B-70—the military prototype of the supersonic transports—it will be of steel. It will be adequately powered. It will be streamlined. It will have comfort—even luxury—and a massive safety and dependability ratio. All this leads to the ultimate question: will it pay off for the commercial manufacturer and airline operator?

The end of the development of this sort of travel on the earth's surface is in plain sight. Since the earth is roughly 25,000 miles around at its greatest circumference, the maximum possible nonstop trip is 12,500 miles. A rocket does this distance in half an hour. It is a trip that means a journey from Honolulu in the Hawaiian Islands to Capetown, South Africa; or from Santiago, Chile, to Bombay, India; or from Melbourne, Australia, to the Azores Islands in the Atlantic; or from Tokyo, Japan, to Buenos Aires, Argentina.

The present DC-8 has a range of less than half this air mileage and does its mileage in about ten hours. Some airlines feel that the pattern of travel may reach its maximum at the DC-8 range and that relatively few people are going to want to travel ten or a dozen thousand miles enough times in the year to make the ultimate distance hops profitable. (Most great cities around the globe are spaced at about half that range or less.) They do believe, however, that a supersonic plane such as the DC-8 presages can better the service by doing the same journey in a third the time.

In order to do this, the trip as a whole must be taken into account. A supersonic vehicle must take off, cruise, and land. Cruising is no problem. It will undoubtedly fly at a height of from 50,000 to 100,000 feet above the earth, choosing its altitude according to the currents. But the take-off and landing present genuine slowdowns of such an operation.

Up to nearly 30,000 feet, any fast take-off will produce not only outrageous noise but a devastating sonic boom in the neighborhood —drastic enough to act almost like the smash of a giant fist. The heat of such a take-off will be considerable. The same applies to the other end of the trip: the vehicle must slow down to re-enter the atmosphere and use the old familiar techniques of clearance, pattern, stacking, and landing. Thus, no matter how much the instrument of travel is improved, even to cruising at the speed of light, it is permanently limited by the conditional visas of leaving and entering the atmosphere.

Any commercial transport of the type of the experimental X-15 rocket plane will have to be tested for an unbelievably long and stress-filled period. It may result in a cruising speed in the high thin air of Mach 10—or 7,600 miles an hour. It will be slim and much smaller than the DC-8. It will probably be built, because of its cost, by combining the assets of a couple of national governments that will use the accumulated wisdom of associated airlines. But Douglas studies show that its fares will be no higher than those for DC-8 in cost per mile.

Such a supersonic vehicle was planned by Douglas as far back as June, 1953. Designs were launched for a "hypersonic manned plane" for the Navy, the D-558-III. It would have been rocket-powered, dropped from a bigger plane at 40,000 feet, and operated as a test carrier for aerodynamics, structural, operational, and human factor problems. It was abandoned as a project in favor of concentrating on the X-15 experiment.

11

There are a group of responsible engineers within Douglas to whom it is "not clear" what purpose such a plane would serve. They point out the narrow corridors of flight that must be hemmed in by aircraft lift requirements and structural heating limitations. One of these is R. L. Johnson, chief engineer for missiles and space. He is of the opinion that the next step may very well be to the pure-rocket passenger-and-cargo vehicle.

"Everything revolves around the power plant," he declares. "What we need is already in existence and simply needs hard work in development: the nuclear rocket engine." A prototype of this engine was tested in 1959 with remarkably good results. "As far as controls go," says Johnson, "as far back as 1957 we lifted a Thor missile up six or seven feet and then set it back down into its pit without a quiver." He believes that the DC-8 is a prototype of the last plane in level atmosphere flight and that the future may turn to high-arc, ballistic flight in the exosphere.

The problems of supersonic flight are mostly bypassed by the rocket idea, he thinks. Given $5,000,000,000 and ten years, it appears feasible that a fleet of ten or twenty such carriers might be built with as sound a guarantee of safety and reliability as the DC-8—"and operated at a lower cost per pound."

The present methods of building embodied in the DC-8 can be used for such a vehicle. The same techniques, together with a variety of materials, even aluminum, can be applied to a rocket. "It will be in the atmosphere only two of three minutes and not have time to get up to even four hundred degrees Fahrenheit," says Johnson. "On re-entry, we merely slow up and sit down as we come in. Even now, control is no problem."

The power would be supplied by an engine built with a small atomic reactor which would heat (and be cooled by) liquid hydrogen—"as easy and perhaps safer to handle than liquid oxygen." The hot, expanding hydrogen would give the propulsion, and at the same time its tanks—plus other materials—would shield the passengers and crew. Radiation for loading and unloading would not be harmful. Landing places would possibly be small uninhabited islands such as San Clemente off the California coast. The pressure on the passengers would never go over two or three G's—three times their own weight—and pilots have already endured as high as fifteen G's.

"Such a vehicle could carry one hundred and fifty people like the DC-8 and make a transcontinental trip in fifteen minutes," says Johnson. "The power would be on for only a very short time and the rocket could coast the rest of the way. The crew would actually be only monitors—most of the control would come from the ground, as in present rocket tests. The engine itself is a killer for space travel—it would make not only earth flights but flights to Mars and moon routine."

It is a fact that the DC-8 and theoretical thinking are coming closer together in space thinking, As far as pressure is concerned, the Big Eight could fly interplanetary routes without change in the fuselage. A round trip to Mars—with minimum acceleration and deceleration—would take only four and a half days, according to A. M. Mayo, former Douglas chief equipment and safety research engineer at El Segundo. The rate of travel would be about a million miles per hour. This leaves only the structural beefing-up—and the unknown hazards of space—to come.

It was not that way in the first days of flying. Then, up and down or sideways, the headaches and the grief were the sole, undisputed property of a handful of men. One of them was a man named Donald Wills Douglas.

T W O :

THE HIGHLANDER'S FLING

1

IN 1945, Donald Douglas laid down the qualifications for the top men in his business. He issued a handbill entitled *What I Look for in an Executive.*

It said in part: "Primarily, I seek a warm, balanced human being. Successful leaders in business or industry need other characteristics, too. They must be friendly, well adjusted, with sympathetic understanding of human motives, limitations, weaknesses, and strength. They must have a lust for life, inherent enthusiasm, impersonal curiosity in things and people, and a faith in the men and women they direct. Good executives must have judgment, self-confidence, a sense of justice tempered with kindness, an instinct for teamwork, a sense of fair play, and a talent for helping and teaching their associates."

Douglas was talking about other people, not himself. Many of the qualities he mentions are missing from his own make-up. But some intangible ingredient, which is not listed, has created the Douglas Aircraft Company of just such people as he describes.

To select a single quality of the complex personality of this man—a symbol of the whole—is impossible. He is the foremost figure of an industry that is the weirdest chaos in the world of finance and finagling, of genius and goofs, of luck and labor—of long experiment and sudden revelation. Douglas himself is so bound up with his forty years in aircraft manufacture that his character necessarily shares all the flaws and virtues of its existence.

In a sea of stress, where ultimate decisions involving as much as $500,000,000 must be made, he is a rock of fortitude. His craggy brown face, salt-and-pepper hair, his unpressed suits of orange-brown tweed, his penetrating blue eyes and grim mouth are the scene of the final court of appeal for any aeronautical scheme.

Not everyone agrees with him. He has had failures, and men have made fortunes by doing what he has refused to do. But he commands a sort of awed respect from anyone who knows airplanes.

He is a man who started in 1920 with $600 in capital in the rear of a Santa Monica, California, barbershop. Within twenty-four years, his eighteen square feet of desk space had ballooned to six great factories in three states, with a total floor space of 16,277,384 square feet. Instead of himself alone, he had an organization of 160,000. He had orginally paid himself nothing, but in 1944 he had a payroll of more than $400,000,000. From a set of penciled specifications on brown paper, he had come to producing goods annually valued at more than a billion dollars.

In those days in 1944—at the height of World War II—Douglas was not only the world's tycoon of aircraft manufacturing, he was actually the fourth biggest company in the United States. His output during the war years was 29,385 planes—one sixth of the total American effort in airframe pounds.

No one who knows these achievements can afford to underestimate the man who set such forces in motion in so short a time. Like him or not—and there are some who have reservations—the name of Douglas is a part of the history of the country he helped establish and preserve. It is a name that ranks with the last of the great pioneers.

2

On a clear day, the kind of day that it is a delight to fly, the shadow of Douglas stretches out to the horizon. It does not resemble its burly cause; it is thin and streamlined. If the Old Man, as he is called, were to cock his arms akimbo, the shadow might even resemble the swept-back wings of the DC-8, possibly the last great airliner that he will ever help to create.

The time is not far when he will retire from the aircraft industry. At the age of sixty-six, in 1958, he saw the first DC-8 take off on Memorial Day. He has had a major share in that major revolution in man's common history: the invasion of the air. Although he commenced his operations seventeen years after the first flight of the Wright brothers and eleven years after the United States Army bought its first plane, he was a vital part of the fabulous decade of air advances that began in 1919 with the crossing of the Atlantic by A. C. Read, the flight of Ross Smith from London to Australia, the Byrd-Bennett flight over the North Pole in 1926, the Lindbergh thirty-three-hour solo over the Atlantic in 1927, the Pacific crossing of Charles Kingsford–Smith the following year, and the eight-day-plus flight around the world by Post and Gatty in 1931. Indeed, the first world "cruise" by a squadron of Army pilots was made in 1924 in the three World Cruiser seaplanes built by Douglas himself. His feelings about such a success came to the fore during the work on his next order for the Army, the XO-2 observation plane. Douglas tacked the government citation for the WC feat on the company bulletin board and chalked below it:

"Men: The above is for each one of you. On the XO-2 you have done your part. If she don't win, it is my fault. Thanks. Doug."

What that scribble meant was a policy of dispersing credit and focusing responsibility. Douglas had designed the WC's (they later became his trade-mark, a world globe with three planes circling it). He had done the same for the XO-2. He was willing to let the credit go and take the blame.

What he was building, in those early days, was more than a fuselage of wood, steel, and canvas. It was a crate for his own uncompromising beliefs and standards. He was taking the first steps upward on the scale of aeronautical evolution which even he saw only dimly ahead.

What in his background produced this combination of conservatism and integrity in one of the most reckless ventures in the development of man, is hard to guess. It is probably inexplicable to Douglas himself—how he can both gamble and hedge with the same abandon. But it remains true that the Douglas company is one of the few organizations in American industrial history whose existence has run parallel with the life of its creator.

No one else runs Douglas but Douglas. All important decisions are, in the final analysis, referred to the granitic Old Man himself. Douglas has warmed the seat of every executive chair in the outfit—founder, chief designer, president, chief executive, and board chairman. Now he is becoming a trifle weary of the load; he is turning over the direction of his vital force in aviation to his son, a pleasant, hard-driving young executive of forty-three, Donald Douglas, Jr.

"Let him make the decisions," he says. "One of these days I'll just disappear from the plant. Like steam off hot water."

3

Still, the laborious facts of history cannot be displaced. In the long life of Douglas in aeronautics, climaxed by the creation of the DC-8, he has won a place that is not even challenged by any other manufacturer. In a few instances, the first Douglas commercial planes he ever built are still flying; the bodies and wings he constructed (Douglas has never built a single airplane engine) are so stout that they have survived as many as fifty engine changes. His extraordinary DC-3 has risen to the status of a flying legend. As late as 1958, more than 52 per cent of all commercial aircraft were built by Douglas. More than half the millions of passengers who climbed into all planes signed an unwritten declaration of faith in Douglas, the man who made them.

Douglas was born April 6, 1892, with a small silver spoon in his mouth. His father was a third-generation Scotsman, a Brooklyn banker, who was never altogether convinced that aeronautical engineering was a proper career. He remained doubtful to the day of his death in 1958, at the age of ninety-five.

The family name of Douglas—famous in Scotland—is from the Gaelic *dhuglas,* "the dark waters." The family coat-of-arms includes a human heart and a wing. The boy wrote and published poems at the age of fifteen (and still writes them in his spare time). The same year, in 1907, the War Department asked for bids on a plane "supported entirely by the dynamic reaction of the atmosphere."

The first love of the boy was sailing on Long Island Sound, an avocation he has pursued ever since. His other hobby was a passion for reading. Douglas is still likely to quote Robert Burns when deeply moved, and he can rouse Shakespeare from the shades if the occasion merits it. Asked to finance a hack writer to do his biography, Douglas replied in learned disgust: "Only a fool, as Max Beerbohm said, would pay money to have someone write about him."

Douglas had other interests, closer to what proved to be his lifework. He was eleven when the Wright brothers made their historic excursion into space, and the accounts enthralled him. But his interest in sailing induced him to try for admission to the Naval Academy. In 1909, he was duly made a cadet. He discovered he had already formed his principles; he was shocked that Annapolis offered no courses in the precocious business of flying. His inclination was neither for land nor water but for the air. He took unauthorized time off from his studies to watch openmouthed while the Wrights demonstrated their newfangled device at Fort Myer, Virginia. He put his own models together with spit-and-paste and flew them out of his dormitory window. Douglas even experimented with some early theories of jet propulsion. "I conducted one of these experiments myself in my brother's room while I was still at Annapolis," he says. "It was sort of a gunpowder jet that I designed and attached to a chair. The result, if not practical, was quite spectacular, and it left its mark, mostly black, over a considerable area of the room."

Jet-propelled chairs were far in the future. In that era Douglas could not induce the Navy to institute classes in aeronautics. When he became a junior, he heard about the Massachusetts Institute of Technology courses. Despite his high marks, he promptly quit Annapolis in 1912. At MIT he came under the tutelage of a brilliant teacher of things aerial, Jerome Hunsaker, who taught him the lore of aviation engineering. He shot through the course in two years, graduating with a Bachelor of Science in 1914.

4

Douglas' own flying ability was not part of his education. He never was—as in the case of Martin and the others—a member of the select aviator groups. He never entered a plane until 1915. He did not get his pilot's license until 1924, when he was thirty-two years old. Martin, on the other hand, had become famous for his flights with movie stars. On one occasion, he had taken up Mary Pickford, the sweetheart of the screen, only on her mother's admonition: "Don't you dare fly over two thousand feet. If something goes wrong and you fall down, I don't want Mary hurt."

But Douglas had an uncanny practical sense about what would and would not fly in those jerry-built years. He worked closely with Hunsaker at MIT for a year, helping him instruct. He became consultant to a newly formed aircraft company in Connecticut and, finally, in 1916, on the strength of a recommendation from Hunsaker, he was appointed chief engineer for the Glenn L. Martin Company in Cleveland, Ohio.

Before he was well settled into his executive seat, Douglas was rudely ousted by the entrance of the United States into World War I. He became chief civilian aeronautical engineer for the Signal Corps—which then had command of the aviation forces—only to return in a year to the Martin company. But in that single year he had made a name for himself: his original design for the Martin military bomber had started the Army thinking seriously about the possibilities of strategic air power. It was the Martin plane that was used by Brigadier General William L. Mitchell to prove his thesis that an aerial bomb could sink a battleship—a feat accomplished off New Jersey, in 1921.

5

In the Cleveland plant of Martin, Douglas found himself in disagreement with Lawrence Bell, the factory manager, over design. Douglas had a more conservative approach than either Martin or Bell (who was later to become famous as a designer in his own right). His theories about protecting the payload of human beings and his dreams about planes as a basic means of transport did not jibe with the then-popular notions of them as simple machines in the Great Experiment with expendable pilots. It was amicably agreed that Douglas would leave.

He emigrated to California with his few hundred dollars, his wife, two children, and a dog. He was obliged to hoe potatoes and wash cars for a while in order to keep himself in funds, but he was making new friends and solid business contacts. His delay in picking up customers gave him the patina of pessimism that has marked his career since then.

His luck had not entirely run out. He encountered a young, wealthy, hell-for-leather sportsman named David R. Davis. Davis was eager to make headlines. He offered Douglas $40,000 for a racing plane that would fly nonstop across the United States. Douglas promptly hired the second story of a shop near the Los Angeles railroad station. He wrote back East and got six young former Martin associates to pledge their futures with him. He built the plane with tools borrowed from a piano shop downstairs. The finished product was lowered down an elevator shaft in sections, trucked out to the Goodyear dirigible hangar in East Los Angeles, and there assembled.

Douglas' talent for design did not fail him. He had formed a company, the Davis-Douglas Company, with his backer, and their product proved worthy of its maker. On a test flight it went up to 19,160 feet, an altitude record nearly double that on the books. Davis took off for his cross-country hop, and the plane (with its hired pilot) managed to get 785 miles in 8 hours and 45 minutes, deep into Texas. There it crashed. It had to be shipped back to California for repairs. While it was waiting for parts, two Army pilots shot across the country and Davis disgustedly called the deal off.

With supreme faith in his own work, Douglas bought a railroad ticket to Washington and struck boldly into the ranks of his old Annapolis acquaintances. He wanted to persuade them that his first creation—called the *Cloudster*—was capable of being transformed at minimum cost into a dreadful weapon from the air called a "torpedo bomber." The unique idea as much as the design intrigued the Navy. He offered them three planes for the special price of $119,000. They accepted.

6

Back in the sprouting city of Los Angeles with the orders, Douglas found himself stymied. Aviation was evidently an unheard-of business, promoted and financed by madmen. No reputable banker would give him a penny. Douglas' own juvenile looks and shy mannerisms did not help his selling technique. Douglas began to sink once more into the morass of despair that had afflicted him before.

His luck changed when he ran into a cheery individual named

Bill Henry. Henry, then a sports writer and now a columnist for the Los Angeles *Times,* had known him from the days when he and Douglas had both been working for Martin. They had a mutual admiration and an affection for California. Here is Henry's own account of his association with Douglas and what came of it:

"I became acquainted with Donald Douglas in 1919, when Martin asked me to come to Cleveland on a temporary basis to assist him in his public relations. Douglas was his chief engineer. Having previously worked at the Martin plant in Los Angeles, he was anxious to get back. When I finished my six-month stint in Cleveland, I returned to Los Angeles and, frankly, couldn't see much prospect of raising money for Douglas. I was, you understand, only interested then—as now—in my job as a reporter.

"Douglas expected Davis, a personal friend of his, to finance the prospective government contract, but Davis refused and Doug was desperate—he had a contract for three torpedo planes for about $117,000 and had a very favorable contract which, he estimated, would require only about $15,000 to carry it. He came to me in desperation and I took him to see Harry Chandler (owner of the *Times*), who took my word for it that Douglas knew what he was doing. He wrote a letter offering to guarantee 10 per cent of what Douglas might need and gave us a list of other Southern Californians who, he said, ought to help out. We interviewed enough to get the necessary guarantees, borrowed the money from Security Bank, and Douglas was on his way.

"I had no arrangement to participate and never had any intention of getting into the airplane business. I helped Doug in any way possible, filling in as a vice-president when he formed a company but never actively participating except as a friend. He got another good contract—this one from the Army for the planes which eventually were first to fly around the world—and moved his plant to an old movie studio located on Wilshire Boulevard in Santa Monica.

"By this time his business was going along well and he needed some expert assistance in management and brought in a friend from the East. I thought this was a good time to concentrate on my newspaper duties and told Doug so. He said that he had always greatly appreciated my assistance (I had never had a job nor drawn any pay from the Douglas Company) and insisted that he had set aside a share in the company for me and that he wanted me to keep it. I told him that everything I had done was on a basis of friendship and that I did not want to become involved in anything but the newspaper business, but he insisted on giving me a considerable amount of money, which, he said, represented what he believed was the value of my service. I took it with pleasure.

"Frankly, my contribution was very small and the success of the company was due, from the beginning, to his skills and his contacts with the right people in government. The real hero of the early days of Douglas was Chandler, who established Doug's credit with the bank and needled leading citizens into going on Doug's note as a public service to get the airplane industry established in Southern California. He asked nothing from Douglas in return and required that the other guarantors should participate on the same basis. As a result, when Douglas really was firmly established, he was sole owner of the company."

Douglas did not have a happy time producing the planes. Paydays were forgot. Until late at night the wives of his associates sewed fabrics onto the wings. The $15,000 was not due until delivery of the planes, and Douglas himself was short enough to be forced to do odd jobs and borrow money. His workers even pooled the funds and paid for a blowout on one of his Ford's tires so that he could come to work.

The trio of planes was delivered. They were eventually accepted. The check came in; a celebration was due. Months before, recruiting his friends from back East to help him, he had written that there was no assurance of success with him but that if they came they would "share well at the table if anything comes of it in a bigger way." Douglas kept his promise. Each one of those original employees (except one who quit) stayed with him—two to their dying day—without missing another check.

7

Looking back at those years, the days when the pilots traipsed into the skies in anything from kites to crates, it seems incredible that aviation could have been so adventurous. One can believe in the horror of the bankers who were asked to finance what then appeared to be "stunts" and later turned out to be the instinctive trail blazing of the dedicated.

Record after record was created, broken, and re-created. A pilot's log for the single year of 1929 would give an astounding number of achievements that foreshadowed almost all the later necessities of aeronautical development.

Bernt Balchen flew Commander Byrd over the South Pole. The Army flew a trimotored Fokker (with Spaatz, Eaker, and Quesada) over Los Angeles for nearly 151 hours; then their record was broken four times in the same year, the last time with the single-motored plane that stayed up more than 420 hours and was refueled 47 times. A Long Beach pilot stayed up alone for more than 38 hours; a Frenchwoman remained aloft alone for 26 hours. Eight flights were attempted over the Atlantic: two French, two Spanish, two American, one Polish, and one Swiss. Three of them failed, and two of them—one Swiss and one American—were never heard of again.

The famous Schneider Trophy race was held for the eleventh time, and boosted the speed record from 45 miles per hour in 1913 to more than 328 miles in 1929. It was a record broken again in the later months, by the English who raised it to nearly 358 miles per hour.

Cross-country flights were common. Captain Frank Hawks made it from coast to coast and back again in just under forty-four hours. Windsor, Canada, and Havana, Cuba, were connected by nonstop flights; so were Moscow, Alaska, and New York by a Russian crew that covered 12,500 miles. An English pair flew nonstop from Lincolnshire, England, to Karachi, India, 4,130 miles in under

51 hours. Coste and Bellonte roared from Paris to Tsitsihar, Man-churia, a distance of 5,500 miles, nonstop.

A Navy pilot named Soucek flew to a height of more than 39,000 feet and lost the record two weeks later to a German aviator who plunged upward to 41,704 feet. The Germans also flew the Dornier DO-X, the biggest airplane in the world and a harbinger of the future. It weighed 52 tons, seated 169 people, carried fuel for 750 miles, and flew at a rate of 110 miles an hour. A Diesel-powered plane flew 650 miles for a cost of $4.68. Gliders rose to 7,231 feet and stayed in the air for as long as 14 hours and 45 minutes. Lieu-tenant James Doolittle took off and flew and landed his plane on Long Island—flying absolutely blind, with only his instruments as his all-seeing "eyes."

It was a time of enormous excitement for aviation circles. In the midst of it, Douglas pondered and looked into the future. Almost unnoticed was the fact that there were already thirty-two airlines in the cargo business, forty-seven carrying mail, and sixty-one carrying passengers. There were slightly more than 29,000 miles of estab-lished airways, with about a third of that ready for night flying. It made a deep impression on the young designer that the number of airplane miles flown had jumped from under six million in 1927 to nearly ten million in 1928. The revenue from mail contracts during the same period had leaped from about two and a half million dollars to about seven and a half million. In 1927, there had been virtually no revenue at all from passengers and cargo; but over $500,000 had been recorded in 1928.

Here was an untapped field, one that would pay real dividends to anyone who had the vision to exploit it. More than that, the value of "air products" had jumped from approximately $21,000,000 in 1927 to the surprising total of more than $64,000,000 in 1928. The conclusion was plain: people were being sold on air transport. There was a big and growing market for the kind of airplanes that would supply their needs.

8

Today, it is estimated, every six seconds somewhere in the world a Douglas transport plane takes off. The paternalistic empire of Douglas, which includes technicians in virtually every major country on the globe to keep the immense fleets of planes flying, has been established. Whatever his faults of brusqueness or clannishness—his four sons and his lone daughter will probably uphold the tradition—Douglas has built his regime on a personal basis. During the depression he kept on six hundred employees who merely manicured the little plant that had no plane orders to fill. He ignored production-line techniques if they interfered with his old retainers, allowing them to work at their own sweet pace. He never personally fired anyone, although he has been forced to some of the most massive "let-go's" in any business.

This strong strain of sentiment which runs through everything he does is an echo of the Scots family ties in his blood. Douglas does not circulate among the social set of Southern California; his recreation had been confined largely to sailing successive windjamming yachts like the *Kinkajou* and the *Endymion* in his younger days and puttering around with a smaller yawl in his later years. Another hobby is his most ancient one of writing doggerel verse and singing Scots ballads to celebrate choice moments.

Although his latent talent for practical jokes has dimmed with the years, the Douglas intimates still tell of the Old Man's gambols with some awe. As the time when the Douglas yacht was pursued by every craft in the channel. The other mariners had spied a nude lady in the rigging. She turned out to be a department-store window mannequin. One that raised outcries of bad sportsmanship came about when Douglas cruised along, apparently followed by an immense swordfish. Those who tried to catch the elusive creature finally discovered it was a wooden fin towed on a long line behind his yacht. It may be only one of his straight-faced gags that makes him tell reporters: "I think flying for pleasure is a bore. I don't like cars or trains, either; the only way to travel is by boat."

9

But Douglas, a precise and sentimental man composed of poet and slide rule in equal parts—who used to sleep with a memorandum pad and an adding machine at his bedside—sometimes overrode his impersonality.

To bolster plant morale in 1938, he organized a bagpipe band. Douglas himself learned how to play the device in a skreeghing fashion. As major-domo, he skirled his way through a succession of yachting parties before he abandoned it. But when the unions tried to organize his plant in 1936, Douglas resisted until the strike collapsed after an abortive sitdown. In the same year, when the United Auto Workers won elections in his two largest plants, Douglas signed his first union contract. Now he works harmoniously with nearly twenty such organizations.

He has asked his employees that if they have a suggestion "not to keep it on ice or let it burn you up. Tell me about it in your own words." But he is a hard man to get to see. When he does allow visitors, he allocates them only a few minutes; but his patience is as noticeable as his efficiency. He works his day in intense fifteen-minute spurts.

His zest for adventure and the unknown still drives him on. He has been shipwrecked twice—once on the Santa Cruz islands, when a gale trapped him in a narrow bay, and once in a small speedboat, when he deliberately rammed a small whale to see what it would do. It did fine: it charged his boat and stove it in. Douglas was rescued on both occasions by his faithful employees, who were in reach of his radio distress calls.

The statement of Douglas in Washington, in January, 1958, was a fair indication of the man's directness and isolated frankness. He asked the Senate preparedness subcommittee pointedly for "more guts and less gobbledegook" in speeding missile and anti-missile activities.

Only a couple of months before, he had made a similar decision

in his own life. He had elevated Donald, Junior, to the presidency
of Douglas. "The Old Man planned and designed Donald just as
he would have engineered a plane," said a subordinate.

<h1 style="text-align:center">10</h1>

What Douglas learned, in the fat and lean periods that alternated
like the meat on the back of a shoat, was that he must establish
standards of long-time performance. He could not hope to create
a business merely by catering to the whims or rich sportsmen or
the fly-by-nights who thought of aviation as simply another great
American fad, or even the fluctuating contracts of the military. He
had to establish his work on a sound footing.

His first move was to plump uncompromisingly for a series of
airplanes rather than one. He had made a series of observation
planes for the Army, the O-2's—and for the advanced O-2H's, he
had got his first million-dollar order. But military favor was not,
he knew, a dependable base for expansion. There was no security
he could see coming from Washington and its periods of crisis and
recession. He commenced the development of the M-1 to M-4
series, the square-engined biplanes that were to become the world's
first airmail planes. Despite their primitive appearance today, the
soundness of their engineering and construction made them the
forerunners of the American air-transport idea.

More than that, Douglas had a continuous panorama of flight
development in his head. He commenced to experiment with a
really large plane, the C-1, a six-passenger transport. He managed
to build it in the late twenties. It flew and flew well—like most of
the Douglas creations—but, while the C-1 was sold to the Army as
a cargo plane in some quantity, there was simply no demand for a
six-passenger transport at that time in aviation history. Douglas
abandoned his dream for the time being.

He returned to the refinement of his design for the O-2 series,
which had become the M-1, and the further exploration of the
torpedo-bomber field. Production of the O-2's commenced in 1925

and continued until 1935, Douglas building a total of 507 planes in this particular series. He had the pleasure of seeing his plane inaugurate the first regular airmail service on April 27, 1926, from Los Angeles to Salt Lake City.

By that time he had concluded his building of the DT (Douglas Torpedo) planes for the Navy. From 1921 to 1924, he had built forty-one of them. They had been steadily improved in the DT-2 and the T2D in 1928; the last of which could be converted for either land or water.

But before he abandoned the production of the Navy planes for the O-2 series, Douglas had become famous for handing over four of his remodeled DT's to the United States Army Air Service (created in 1921). It was his own contribution to the "stunts" of the period that proved to be essential additions to the lore of aviation. These were the planes that were to complete by air what Magellan had done by sea: the first circumnavigation of the world.

11

Douglas had been beaten by two Army pilots in the first long flight with Davis across the United States. He determined to join forces with the military in what was an amazing request asked him in the summer of 1923: a set of planes to go around the world. He designed them all the rest of that season. In the fall he commenced to build. In March, 1924, four of them were assembled and tested.

The request of the Army did not catch Douglas altogether unprepared. As has been the case in every instance since, he had planned ahead. As early as 1915, he had planned a round-the-world flight with a wealthy Boston backer. Now, however, it was a reality with government backing. Among its stated goals were these aspirations:

". . . to demonstrate the feasibility of aerial communication and transportation between the various continents . . . to make the people of the world conscious that aerial transportation is able to meet any and all conditions . . . to arouse interest in aircraft as a vital force in the marts of commerce. . . ."

They were goals of foresight and force. They served Douglas as a text for his own commercial endeavors during the rest of his life.

The wooden 8,000-pound planes could land on sea or land. They could carry about 2,600 pounds of this gross weight, including 450 gallons (18 hours) for flight. The planes were 35 feet long with 50-foot wing spans, and had 400-horsepower engines with a speed of roughly 100 miles per hour.

The planes were to cover twenty-two countries and approximately 25,000 miles. They flew north from Santa Monica and the Douglas plant to Seattle. They started from there on April 5. One plane crashed almost immediately, against a fogbound cliff in Alaska. Another was lost in rough seas off Iceland. A fifth plane joined the remaining two at Nova Scotia and flew in with them to a reception at Santa Monica, Douglas' home town. Two hundred thousand people and an acre of landing room, covered with roses, greeted the pilots.

They had covered 28,945 miles in a flying time of 15 days, 11 hours, and 7 minutes at an average speed of just more than 72 miles per hour.

Despite the applause for his hardy World Cruisers, Douglas had not been idle. He had been designing his XO observation plane. Shortly after the tumultuous ending of the world flight, he won three firsts in three competitions, and the Air Service gave him a $750,000 order for fifty planes. Two years later came the first airmail service, and a month later the same line, Western Air Express, flew two passengers from Los Angeles to Salt Lake City for $90 apiece. The same year Douglas got an order for fifty-one mail planes of the same type.

Some disappointments cropped up. In 1928, Douglas built a luxury plane called the *Ambassador,* intended for sportsmen. It never did sell enough copies to make back its cost. But this disappointment was temporary compared to the sinking feeling he got when he viewed the declining rate of his sales, despite his continuing military orders.

From October, 1930, to July, 1932, the average of production was something more than four planes a week—and only seventy planes were sold in 1932. The economic lash was beginning to be felt by the forty-year-old designer. The honors and accolades were thin stuff. He knew that the narrow profit margins of the government and the endless delays and disputes were not for him. Douglas commenced to think in terms of mail and cargo; of bigger payloads; of the old C-1; and, above all, of those two $90 passengers back in 1926.

THREE:

THE CLASSIC INSPIRATION

1

EARLY one sultry morning in August, 1932, Douglas got a confidential letter. It consisted of two short, prickly paragraphs. It was from Jack Frye, then vice-president in charge of operations for the Transcontinental and Western Airline.

Douglas knew Frye as a bustling, hotly competitive young executive. He knew that Frye knew that he designed and built good airplanes. Both men knew that National Air Transport, an affiliate of the Boeing company, had just bought a fleet of twenty of the $75,000 Boeing 247's. It was a sleek, low-wing transport that could carry ten passengers and cross the continent in nineteen hours. What was needed was a plane as good as the 247—and, if possible, better. "It was the challenge of the 247 that put us into the transport business," said Douglas years afterward.

Frye wrote: "Transcontinental and Western Air is interested in purchasing ten or more trimotored transport planes. I am attaching our general performance specifications, covering this equipment, and would appreciate your advising whether your company is interested in this manufacturing job.

"If so, approximately how long would it take to turn out the first plane for service tests?"

Nowhere in his terse note or in his specifications did Frye betray the slightest interest in price. There was a printed streamer on the letter paper that assumes an ironic air in hindsight. It read: SAVE TIME—USE THE AIR MAIL.

2

The Frye specifications for a transport plane—in the light of today's requirements—seem childish. But in that day, during the bottom of the depression, they appeared monumental. They consisted of the following:

1. An all-metal trimotor plane.
2. Three engines of 500 to 550 horsepower each.
3. A gross weight of about 7 tons.
4. A payload of at least 2,300 pounds, plus 350 pounds for "radio and wing mail-bins."
5. A crew of two, capable of flying a range of 1,060 miles at 150 miles an hour.
6. Room for 12 passengers in comfortable seats, complete instrumentation, night-flying equipment, and the "usual miscellaneous equipment."

Frye was not missing a single chance to trump all the tricks of the Boeing 247. He demanded a top speed of 185 miles per hour, a landing speed of not more than 65 miles per hour, and a minimum ceiling of 21,000 feet—plus the ability to make fully loaded takeoffs at any TWA airport on two engines.

It was a rough request. Douglas was more than interested; he was fascinated. He got to work. In five days he and his three engineering assistants had designed a new kind of plane. They figured the cost of building it while en route to Kansas City to see Frye.

3

In those years the public did not care for planes as a means of traveling. The safety margins were too narrow. Too many crashes had been too well publicized; and public figures of the stature of the great football coach, Knute Rockne, had been killed as short a time before as March, 1931.

The Rockne crash, in which the plane lost a wing in midair, had discredited the transport Fokkers, made in America, which had emerged from the famous fighter plane of World War I. The other mainstays of the airlines, the Ford trimotored "Tin Geese" with their corrugated-iron styling, were reliable enough. But they shook up passengers as if they were in an aerial corncracker. Their cabins stank of semi-explosive gas fumes, and the noise was deafening. Travelers arrived at their destination in a state of shock induced by their trip, as if a giant had done nothing all the way but shout in their ears and rattle their bones. What kept the brave flying was simply the euphoria of flight and the thankfulness to get down safely again. "When you got there, you felt so good about landing that you wanted to go upstairs again," said one air buff with feeling.

Against this disheartening backdrop, Douglas used a unique method of design. He did not call on the technical men alone to create his first prototype of a cargo-passenger plane. Instead, he asked for ideas from everyone within the company. Engineers, pilots, personal friends, and mechanics were asked to list the qualities they thought were needed in an ideal airplane.

From this foot-high mass of fact and moonshine, the most practical suggestions were sorted out. These were refined into what might have been called "ideal general specifications." Then the specialists in aeronautical design were given special tasks.

Basic details were apportioned out. Different men were given the responsibility for the wing, power plant, structure, interior, and similar components. One of the main revisions, which Douglas himself highly approved, was the official heave-ho given to one of the most sacred design theories: the heavy metal beam that transfixed the cabin like an arrow and supported the main weight of the wings. Instead, the wings were engineered to be bolted to the body. Their weight was planned to be distributed by structural design. This radical departure occasionally fretted the passengers who knew about it, but it sharply reduced weight and the noise level. Like other Douglas ideas, it caught on.

The Douglas chief engineer, J. H. "Dutch" Kindelberger, later president of North American Aviation, had been a leader in the hectic conferences that preceded the original design. Included in the debate were men like A. E. "Art" Raymond, Fred Herman, Ed Burton, and Fred Stineman, all engineers or designers who went on to make a special niche for themselves in pioneering modern planes. It had been Kindelberger's idea to use two motors instead of three and to fold them in the new NACA streamlined cowling that cut air resistance by 50 per cent. The others had supplied such additional items as the retractable landing gear and the space and weight economies.

It was Raymond who was responsible for the second of Douglas' innovating ideas. He had never made a transcontinental trip by air until shortly after the conference. He landed, wiggling his teeth, unjointing his legs and arms one by one. He described his adventures in the iron womb of the Ford trimotor in graphic terms.

It was so noisy, he said, that they gave him cotton to stuff in his ears. He had to shout to talk across the aisle. The vibration made his jaws chatter. The higher they went to clear the mountain passes, he added, the colder the cabin got. His feet were freezing. The lavatory in the tail was so small he could barely squeeze through the door. The leather-upholstered, wicker-backed chairs were about as comfortable as a seat on a buckboard wagon, he said. When the plane landed in a puddle, a spray of mud was sucked into the cabin vents and splattered him. He concluded with a heartfelt observation: "No wonder people take the train."

Douglas and his practical Scots mind translated Raymond's ordeal into economics and into his second maxim: the public must travel safely and comfortably—even luxuriously—if air travel was to be made popular and profitable. The result was that even before the DC-1 got off the ground its weight, mostly in plumbing and upholstery, had increased more than a ton to a gross of 17,000 pounds.

4

Douglas got the contract from TWA for a dozen planes at a price of $75,000 apiece. Frye forced him to commit himself to the promise that the first model would be tested within a year.

In eleven months the model DC-1 had its maiden flight. D for Douglas; C for Commercial; and the numeral for the first model of what Douglas hoped would be a long and respected line of planes. The DC-1 did not represent a specific triumph of an individual engineer or even of a group. It was both—a wholly original creation of a group that worked as an organic entity with Douglas himself at the head.

What it did include was a concept of aviation engineering that was to become the fundamental strength of American flight, so basic that in the foreseeable future it cannot be replaced. It was, to a major degree, the simple application of Darwin's theories of natural selection and evolution to the theory of technical plane building.

These principles were that (1) only the better airplanes would survive in the coming era of competition and (2) that each model of a Douglas plane must incorporate in its design the possibilities of a continued evolutionary process. The ghost of the DC-1 still haunts the Douglas design, even that of the climaxing giant, the DC-8.

The original outline of the DC-1 was almost too good to believe at that stage. Even now it is recognized as the vital component of an aeronautical classic which has survived every state of the art, even to the threshold of outer space. But at the same time of its first flight in July, 1933, the wobbly take-off of the prototype did not indicate its inherent worth. The mass ingenuity of the Douglas group had been able not only to meet but surpass all that Frye had ordered. Actually there was only one DC-1. The planes based on it which were built for TWA and others were designated DC-2.

Instead of 150 miles an hour, the cruising speed was 180 miles per hour, using the newest engine in existence, the nine-cylinder

710-horsepower Wright Cyclone. New variable pitch propellers made landings and take-offs safer and easier. The payload weight was improved by 20 per cent. The number of passengers was increased to a total of fourteen.

Most important of all, the number of engines was reduced from a conventional three for a transport to a streamlined two. Their dependability and power were demonstrated by a then-incredible feat. On September 4, 1933, the DC-1 was loaded with almost 18,000 pounds of water ballast at the 4,500-foot-high airport of Winslow, Arizona. It took off. Halfway in its ascent, one engine was cut out. The climb continued normally to 8,000 feet, and the trip was completed over the 220 miles to Albuquerque, New Mexico, without incident. TWA was jubilant. One of their regularly scheduled Fokkers had taken off minutes before the DC-1. The latter had beaten it to Albuquerque by fifteen minutes.

5

In the spring of 1933 there had not been the joy in Douglas that might have been expected. There were predictions that the engines could not get the plane off the ground. The controllable pitch propellers, just perfected, fixed that. The rivalry between Wright and Pratt & Whitney—with chalk lines to divide the separate camps and screens to conceal the motors, and strict security maintained—made the plant look like a battleground. Wright came up with a new cooling fin and cylinder design.

In June, the plane was completed. It looked like a fish (all Douglas models since have shared this resemblance), about 60 feet long, silver-scaled, with big square windows, and 85-foot-long wings mounted beneath the fuselage. The two pilots sat side by side. There were compartments fore and aft for baggage and mail, a big lavatory, a small cooking galley, and a cabin that was soundproof and heated by ducts from the engine. The DC-1 was the biggest and best-looking two-motored transport plane in existence. "Too big," Douglas heard one experienced pilot say. "They won't get her off the ground."

He was nearly right. On its test flight in Santa Monica, 332 days after Frye's letter, the whole Douglas company—swollen now to eight hundred employees—gathered during their lunch hour to see what would happen. "Will she get off?" Douglas anxiously asked Carl Cover, the test pilot. Cover nodded. At 12:36 P.M., the DC-1 was airborne.

6

"There never was an airplane built that wasn't full of bugs," said Kindelberger. "You've got to pick them out one at a time, like hunting fleas on a St. Bernard."

He was right, especially on this occasion. Thirty seconds after the DC-1 had taken off, one engine quit. The other clawed the air, racking the plane; then it quit. Cover nosed the DC-1 down and they caught again. He commenced a series of desperate maneuvers, a jackrabbit in the air, gaining a little with each bound. Finally he got the plane up to 1,500 feet and managed to make his landing. The frantic Wright engineers discovered the carburetor floats were badly mounted. They had cut out the gas every time the plane lifted its head.

A week later, the DC-1 flew again. It commenced fishtailing like a hooked mackerel. More rudder surface and a slight change in the horizontal fin stopped it. A third flight for an inspection of the landing gear while coming down resulted in a stream of sparks, a couple of corkscrewed propellers, and a faceful of tarry pebbles for the inspector. Someone had forgotten to work the hand pump that put down the landing gear.

After more modifications and tests, the DC-1 went up to a ceiling of 21,000 feet. It handled superbly well, but a design consultant from California Institute of Technology passed out at 14,000 feet from lack of oxygen. Douglas began to worry about his passengers. Oxygen masks were no answer. The problems of a pressurized cabin, flying the passengers in a reasonable facsimile of the atmosphere at lower levels, commenced to fill his mind.

A stunt flier imperiled the DC-1 as it rolled to a halt by its hangar. Roaring down in a little biplane, he rolled on his back and buzzed the plane, missing by a few feet. When he landed, the irate Douglas men rushed over to lynch him. The grinning pilot turned out to be Ernst Udet, one of the world's top aerial acrobats and German World War I ace. He wanted to buy the DC-1 model for the European routes of Lufthansa.

Other buyers were intrigued, including Captain Eddie Rickenbacker of Eastern Air Transport, a cousin of TWA. Western Airlines put out feelers on price and performance. The Army Air Corps became interested in the DC-1 as a transport plane and, with modifications, as a bomber tentatively designated as the XB-18. TWA ratified an order for twenty DC-2's, nearly double the number that the original specifications had called for. Frye, who flew the sleek transport for an hour to test it personally, stepped out on the ground with the remark, "This is the sweetest little thing I've ever handled!"

That remark was a profound shock to some of the Douglas staff. It meant that their brain child, the largest twin-motor to date, was already being thought of as too small for the jobs ahead.

The development of the DC-1 had cost $300,000. The contract had specified payment in "gold bullion," and this was scrupulously met after TWA officially took the ship over on September 13. But three years later, when the United States went off the gold standard, Douglas was glad to take the payment in paper money. He had raised the price per plane to $80,000.

7

The debut of the DC-1 had caused not a single ripple in the newspapers of the country. Its first flights were overshadowed by more dramatic aviation news. The Thirteenth Annual National Air Races were in progress. Italo Balbo, the most famous Italian pilot, led a squadron of seaplanes in a mass flight across the Atlantic. Roscoe Turner, the speed ace, roared in from the East to Los Angeles, setting a transcontinental record of 11 hours and 40 minutes.

This last feat was in the minds of two pilots—Frye and Rickenbacker—when they took off from Glendale, California, in a DC-1 on February 18, 1934. Ten days before, President Franklin D. Roosevelt had canceled all commercial airmail contracts—a major blow to the problem of financing aviation development. This was to be the last trip of the mail before the Army Air Corps took over. It was admittedly to demonstrate that "the private operators were better equipped to fly the mail than the Army."

The DC-1 crossed the Rocky Mountains at 14,000 feet, refueled at Kansas City, and ran into bad weather over Ohio. Over the Allegheny Mountains, it encountered a blizzard. Frye took the DC-1 up to 19,500 feet and found a 230-mile tail wind. With its aid, they flashed on to Newark and ended with an elapsed time of 11 hours, 5 minutes—beating Turner's racing-plane mark by fifteen minutes. "This new plane," said a New York newspaper, "has made obsolete all other air-transport equipment in this country or any other."

Douglas was not as disturbed as many others about the loss of the airmail contracts. "We're going to have to make up our minds whether we're going to play pony express or run public carriers," he said. He was of the opinion that there was a lot of money— once the public had been thoroughly sold—in merely carrying passengers. He set out to sell the world on the virtues of his baby.

By the middle of 1935, the DC-1 had nineteen records to its credit, at large in the world and within the United States.

8

A new engine, always the harbinger of a new model of aircraft, came into production in 1934. It was the Wright 1820-F3, which delivered 750 horsepower. Its increased power naturally produced the DC-2, a plane based upon the DC-1 but incorporating minor modifications. The DC-2 was in airline service by the end of 1935; three years later, 138 of these airplanes were in service.

Unlike the DC-1, the latest Douglas model did not lack for publicity. In 1934, one of the first of the DC-2 prototypes was entered in the MacRobertson Air Race, a grind of 10,000 miles from London to Melbourne, Australia. Flown by a Dutch crew of the KLM line (which has used Douglas planes ever since), loaded with mail and a few feckless passengers, the DC-2 won the transport division by a wide margin, in an elapsed time of 90 hours and 13 minutes.

What made this victory genuinely impressive was the fact that the DC-2 came in second in *all* classes. It was beaten only by one other entry, a specially built English pursuit craft made by De Havilland. The margin was 19 hours, 19 minutes.

Nevertheless, the plane had its faults. After its May 14, 1934, delivery to TWA, one of the line's veteran testing pilots nearly upended the transport. He was not acquainted with the new power brakes. Douglas had given them grip enough to make it possible virtually to put a DC-2 down in an acre pasture.

Pilots reported that the auto-pilot had nearly killed them. Investigation proved that a too-heavy oil was being used. The result was that the mechanism stiffened up, so much so that it took the efforts of two burly pilots to bring the plane in.

Worse than that, problems returned to plague the Douglas plant itself. Offering for the first time technical services that virtually guaranteed expert advice for the life of the craft, Douglas found that his passion for quality was driving him to bankruptcy. His efficiency men showed him that he was using up 58,000 man-hours per plane—20,000 more than he could afford if he were to make the barest profit. Hydraulic presses that could stamp out airplane body parts as they did auto bodies solved that riddle without impairing the beginnings of a world-wide Douglas technical coup.

There were some pleasant compliments from abroad. The Fokker buyers, whose planes had been in disrepute since the

Rockne crash, asked for as many DC-2's as they could buy. They admitted the Americans now had the leading transport plane in the world. KLM bought a batch of fourteen before the Fokker deliveries. DC-2's were considered safe enough so that the insurance of pilots was reduced to the cost of that of a pedestrian. An oil company bought a "flying office" complete with desk, filing cabinets, and a telephone. "I thought I had figured all possible markets," Douglas said ruefully, "but this one I really didn't expect."

9

Douglas DC-3! Fourteen Births or Twenty-One Seats! It was a startling sign, but not only for the misprint. Two years and five months after he had hippety-hopped the first DC-1 on its test flight, Cover took up a new plane called the DC-3. Nothing happened that was out of the ordinary: the DC-3 appeared to be that remarkable creation, a plane without bugs.

The years have proved this to be very nearly true. The DC-3 was nothing like the bolt-from-the-blue that was the DC-1; nor was it the strongly modified DC-2. It had none of the high inventiveness and imagination that had marked the building of the former, nor was it as cranky on occasion as the latter. It was simply there in embryo, waiting to be built and to do its job.

As usual, the midwife of the DC-3 was a new engine. Pratt & Whitney and Wright had both improved their products, boosting them to a 1,000-horsepower output. Whereas the DC-2 had operated with a total of 1,420 horsepower for take-off, an empty weight of 12,000 pounds, and a take-off gross weight of 18,000 pounds, the DC-3 had 2,000 horsepower, an empty weight of 14,000 pounds, and a take-off gross weight of 22,000 pounds. Passenger capacity had risen from 14 to 21. The speed boost was from 175 miles per hour to 195.

Raymond called the DC-3 a "stretched version of the DC-2." Douglas thought of it at the time as the "ultimate in air transportation." It was neither of these, as it proved: it was simply the most used, the most dependable, and the most loved airplane ever built. It became the great original classic of the cargo-and-passenger vehicle.

The original specifications of the DC-3 called for two 750-horsepower Pratt & Whitney engines to lift a plane with a gross weight of 24,000 pounds including 21 passengers. It had a wing span of 95 feet and a pudgy shape which rose to nearly 15 feet. Its length was a finicky 64 feet, 5½ inches. It could cruise from 165 to 180 miles per hour, a burbling speed that cut the coast-to-coast time to 15 hours only three years after the racy Boeing 247 had cut it to 19 hours. It could deliver a payload of 4,000 pounds at 1,300-mile range.

Its qualities were almost instantly recognized by the members of the air fraternity. Although the DC-3 cost a rousing $120,000 as against the $85,000 of the DC-2, orders commenced to pile up. One airline, American, converted itself entirely to DC-3's.

The first two DC's had turned many skeptics to the cause of air transport. Before them, air travel and air freight were certainly possible. Before the DC-3 they were inherently probable. But the experience that had been built into this new plane proved to be its own guarantee of delivery of human life and goods.

The traffic which had been waiting so patiently for evidence that speed, safety, and dependability could be achieved in the air instantly came to life. Although a great many DC-2's were still flying (some of the latter were in service as late as 1954, and are still undoubtedly used in odd corners of the world), the DC-3 planes were snatched up as they came hot off the assembly line. By 1936, the 803 specimens of the DC-3 carried 95 per cent of all commercial civilian air traffic. Three years later, it still held more than 90 per cent of this load to its bosom.

What insured its own peculiar accolade—combined of affection, respect, and admiration from passengers, technicians, and pilots—came with the beginning of World War II.

10

General Dwight D. Eisenhower, commanding the combined Allied forces that finally ended the war, named the amphibious "duck" as one of the chief instruments of victory, and added: "Incidentally, four other pieces of equipment that most senior officers came to regard as among the most vital to our success in Africa and Europe were the bulldozer, the jeep, the 2½-ton truck, and the C-47 airplane. Curiously enough, none of these is designed for combat."

The stubby profile of this plane, with its flexible "flapping" wings, became by far the best-known silhouette of any in the world. A total of 10,125 DC-3's were built for military service— to be known under special designations such as C-47's, R4D's, and Dakotas. They proved their airworthiness under every possible flying condition on the planet.

If further proof were needed of the unique value of this aircraft in war and peace, it is enough to say that as late as 1952 more than 3,500 DC-3's out of a total of 11,000 were still in active service. The greatest tribute that can be paid it in the engineering sense is the fact that, although the design is more than a quarter of a century old, no other aircraft has ever been developed capable of equaling its feats in short-stage operations.

Legends have always grown up around great men. In this air-minded generation, legends have encrusted a great machine, the DC-3. A few of them may illustrate the love and faith that the pilots felt in these old "Dizzy Threes," or "Daks," or, with pathetic aerodynamic simplicity, "Old Fatso."

The one known as "Old Miscellaneous" came home from the Far East after long and honorable service. She flew two thousand missions and wore out a dozen engines. She returned home with new wing tips, elevators, and rudders, the last of six changes. With her venerable body came the note: "This is the oldest, fastest C-47 [DC-3] in the Southwest Pacific. Into whatever hands she falls, treat her kindly, and she will always get you to your destination."

Another, flying the famous Hump in the China-Burma-India theater of World War II, got zoomed up to 28,000 feet from a cruising level of 16,000 feet. Just as suddenly, she dropped four miles straight down, to 6,000 feet. The shaken pilot reported: "We stopped with such a jar I couldn't believe a plane could be built to take that kind of punishment."

The saga of "Whistling Willie" is famous but often incorrectly told. In 1942, a DC-3 was riddled by Japanese strafers. Engines, propellers, tires, and all systems were replaced. More than one thousand bullet holes were patched with canvas. It was then flown from Chungking to India with sixty-one refugees. The patches loosened in a monsoon rain and tore off in the wind. The ship became a banshee of the sky. On the landing after the two-hour flight, the welcoming major commented: "You didn't need to radio ahead. We could hear you coming for fifty miles!"

More than one DC-3 has flown more than 10,000,000 miles and has been in service for twenty-five years. An airline plane lost five feet of a wing in a midair collision and landed its full load of passengers without a scratch. Another in China during World War II lost her wing in a Japanese strafe on the runway; another wing, five feet shorter (from a DC-2), was fitted on, and the "DC-2½" flew very well.

Possibly seventy airlines still use DC-3's. About 600,000,000 passengers have been carried safely to their destination. Middle Eastern hegiras take 45, instead of the regulation 21; European airlines schedule 36 seats. One, in the evacuation of Burma, carried 74 passengers. Another, during the 1947 partition revolts in India, took 105 refugees.

The allowable gross take-off weight of the DC-3 is 25,200 pounds. During World War II, the Army Transport Command regularly flew it out with an overload of 31,000 pounds—double the payload. In 1942, the Army flew the South Atlantic with a squadron loaded with 35,000 pounds—mostly highly explosive aviation gasoline.

In Western Australia, which is without railroads, the DC-3

regularly serves more than 500,000 desolate square miles. It flies with fine impartiality purebred bulls, movie stars, geologists and live crayfish, aborigines and aerial surveyors. Such planes have hauled the latest fashions from New York to New Orleans and returned with a load of fresh shrimp. They even hauled five planefuls of coal from New York to Cuba during a dock strike.

A DC-3 was abandoned on a glacier in Iceland. Drifts swallowed it up, and the operators of a small airline there bought the "salvage" for $1,600. Come spring, they found the airplane had melted into the clear. They tractored a runway and took off. The plane is still flying.

One DC-3 was credited with a Japanese Zero fighter. Rammed into some palm trees by the latter, it managed to land although all but eighteen inches of its rudder was chewed away. The Zero crashed. A formation collision tore a fifteen-foot hole in the top of another, but it landed happily. In 1957, a downdraft caused a DC-3 to clip a mountain peak and lose twelve feet of its left wing. It landed safely at the next airport with twenty-three aboard.

A South African restaurateur was so enamored of the DC-3 fame that he bought a war-surplus specimen and mounted it above his hostel. It stayed there for twelve years. It was finally spotted by a practical sentimentalist of the United States, bought, restored —and is still in the air.

In time the DC-3 engine power was increased to 1,200 horsepower. The passenger capacity swelled to twenty-eight, as a tight fit. But the general specifications remained the same. Indeed, carried away by their original success, the company tried to better it in the early 1950's. They announced and produced a "Super DC-3," but they found there was no such animal. The "Super" had a new wing and tail, and was a faster plane than the old favorite, plus a smattering of minor improvements; but no one wanted it. The Navy admittedly bought a substantial number of the "Supers." The airlines went right on using the old reliable model.

The production of this waddling little queen of the skies had come about in the first place because the carriers wanted a "sleeper" plane to match the Pullmans of the railroad. The DC-3 had been enlarged and improved with this in mind, but the final version used the interior only for seating. Nevertheless, the DC-3 did manage to become the all-time sleeper of the plane-manufacturing business.

According to Douglas, the DC-3's have flown an estimated one hundred billion passenger-miles and perhaps one hundred million hours in the air—without including any of the wartime military operations. In 1953, the Civil Aeronautics Board "indefinitely" prolonged the DC-3 airworthiness certificate. There have been numberless citations and compliments paid to "The Gooney Bird," as she was known in one of her many avatars, but possibly the most accurate was that given in August, 1953, by the Secretary of the Air Force Harold E. Talbott. He said: "It unquestionably ranks as the best single airplane ever built."

The one Douglas likes best, that sets down the fundamental reason why the DC-3 was created, is the statement by C. R. Smith of American Airlines: "The DC-3 freed the airlines from complete dependence upon government mail pay. It was the first airplane that could make money by just hauling passengers."

FOUR:

"A CAPABILITY OF GROWTH"

1

THE DC-3 ended the greatest single danger of aviation in its early stages of commercial growth. It was, as one pilot put it, "the danger of starving to death." Not only the burgeoning airlines but also the military were delighted with it. Quantities of the plane were being bought and exuberantly tested. One Army report said that "the aircraft finally broke up under loads three times its design limitations." Without budgeted money for any substantial troop-carrier or cargo-plane force, the DC-3's were purchased by the Air Corps as "generals' personal aircraft" and rechristened the "C-47."

The fuselages were redesigned with heavier floors, provisions for big cargo doors, rows of bucket seats, racks for parapacks, and improved power and instrumentation. One engineer's report of the time read dolefully:

"The C-47 [DC-3] is redesigned to carry airplane engines, propellers, large pieces of cargo, jeeps, small field guns, litters, paratroops, and miscellaneous cargo. The cabin has no lining, the comfortable chairs have been replaced by troop benches, the floor is strongly reinforced, the passenger door is replaced by a large cargo door, and many other incidental changes have been made."

At the time fewer than a thousand of the DC-3 planes had been manufactured. But the tempo of their production was rising steadily. War was in the air. The DC-2's and -3's took off in the first line of defense, carrying high-priority officials and defense shipments just after the Nazi invasion of Poland in 1939. The British called the Lend-Lease C-47 the "Dakota." The Russians copied it as an Ilyushin model. It is still a mainstay of their airlines. Even the busy, busy Japanese got hold of one and commenced making their own reproduction. The gathering war clouds of the world had prompted the speech of President Franklin D. Roosevelt about "quarantining" the aggressor. He called for the building of fifty thousand planes a year.

Douglas spoke four words as one of the leading manufacturers and the spokesman of his fellows. "We can do it," he said. His laconic confidence became the watchword of the industry. Perhaps he had a little more to back it up than the others, having the DC-3 in the air and his geared-up production line on the ground.

A week after Pearl Harbor, DC-3's were moving thousands of troops from secret assembly points in Florida to bases in South America, to make sure of that southern bastion. Orders came in to manufacture the DC-3's by thousands rather than by dozens. One assembly line set up in Oklahoma City never stopped, twenty-four hours a day, for years. By the middle of 1944, the DC-3's were being built at a rate of 1.8 planes a day.

2

World War II, with the DC-3, was the real making of Douglas. The natural offspring of the DC-1 and -2 had most of the inherited virtues and few of the vices of its progenitors. Although it did not give the manufacturer a war bonanza on the financial side, it produced and extended that most intangible asset, public approval and a feeling of total security about airplanes. But the advances could not stop with that.

As far back as 1936, Douglas and his engineers had already been trying doodles on paper with a version of a new plane modeled on the DC-3 success. It was an experimental three-tailed job called the DC-4E. It borrowed heavily from another experimental model, the military bomber called B-19. An effort to please four airlines— Eastern, American, United, and Pan American—it was supposed to be the first of a bigger and faster plane to bring in more revenue.

The $3,000,000 spent upon the DC-4E might have been better invested ten years later. The plane had new and powerful engines, new electrical systems, underwing refueling, retractable tricycle gear, air-conditioned and pressurized cabin, and an assortment of other original thoughts. Such ideas are commonplace today. Then they were too new to be reliable. The technological skills to perfect them had not yet been developed.

Only one prototype was built. Regretfully, the five parties involved wrote the DC-4E off as a loss. The design and the plane itself were a success, but it was an economic failure. It simply could not be flown with profit, unlike the DC-3, which could be built for seven dollars a pound and pay for itself a hundred times over. Only the Japanese liked the portly, square-windowed craft. They bought it for $180,000 in 1939. No one knows the fate of this Douglas model. One story out of the Far East claims that an inexperienced Japanese crew crashed it in Tokyo harbor shortly before the war.

"We should have known better, but we were anxious to push ahead," says Raymond. One point was clear, however, as he pointed out to all concerned: "Our progress must come by evolution of sound, well-developed principles." So, in the language of the engineers, "we sharpened our pencils again" and started over— this time with a "clearer understanding of both design and operational commonsense."

3

The DC-3 was still flying and still being produced in massive quantities. But as far as Douglas was concerned that particular plane was in the past. The designers started work on two more— one called the DC-4 and another called the DC-5.

Again, in the DC-5, the engineers tried to go back to the remarkable DC-3 design, as perfect and classic to an aeronautical engineer as the design of the Greek Parthenon to an architect. They found they could not improve upon it. In many respects the DC-5 simply took over the systems and structural developments of the DC-3, enlarging and improving. There was one radical change; the wing was placed high on the body rather than below, as in the case of the DC-3.

This one change created a greater empty weight. Although the plane was considered a "perfectly satisfactory piece of equipment" by itself, it could not match the payload and range of the DC-3. Only a few of the DC-5's managed to be sold before World War II broke out. Douglas never returned to the idea. Says Raymond dryly: "The experience left us in no doubt that airline operators are strongly influenced by economics."

This left the company with the inevitable choice of a new and drastic departure from the old concepts. It was evident that if any future DC-4 was to become competitive in design, efficiency, and function with the DC-3, it would simply have to be a different plane. Once again, the pencils were sharpened and the minds uncluttered for a new look at the sky.

What appeared was a plane that was almost totally produced during the war and that established records fully comparable to those of the DC-3. Like the DC-1, the DC-4—or C-54 in military parlance—was the hotbed of a new advance. "We found," Raymond says, "that the design of this airplane was straightforward, workable, and, as we learned, capable of considerable growth." He might have added that it was both economical and efficient to operate.

The DC-4 fulfilled a special dream of Douglas himself. In the days when he had got his first order from the Navy, he had two items of equipment with him: a typewriter and a drafting board. He needed one to write the contract and the other to make any changes required. Now, with his 167,000-man force busily turning out DC-3's, he did not need to worry about the typewriter. In his head, his drafting board was still working at top speed.

In the years before the war, Douglas had become an early convert to the idea of land planes flying over the oceans. He had been a pioneer in flying boats, but he knew they had radical limitations. Now that the reliability of power plants and design had been proved by such feats as thirty-eight daily flights from California across the Pacific Ocean—flights that literally clogged the skies— he felt the feat of the land-and-sea World Cruisers in 1924 had significance for commercial transport. He determined to make the DC-4 the world's foremost overseas carrier.

How well he succeeded is in the record. Before the C-54's finished, they had completed nearly 100,000 ocean trips, the "principal ocean hopper," according to General James H. Doolittle. Going into service in 1942, the "Skymaster" proved to be an unusually fruitful source of transport know-how. A four-engined, low-wing, high-tailed bulky plane, it had a total thrust of 5,800 horsepower and a cruising speed of 230 miles per hour. Design refinements increased its empty weight from 37,650 pounds to 51,000 pounds, but these in turn increased the gross weight from 62,000 pounds to 93,000 pounds—a gain of about 50 per cent in payload. It proved its superlative worth and dependability to all the world in the 1948 Berlin Airlift and again in the Korean War of 1950.

4

The DC-4 caused a genuine revolution in aeronautical thinking. Before the war only five four-engined commercial planes had been flown in the United States. These had been bought up by the Army in 1941. By the end of the war in 1945, the surplus planes of the Air Corps were to be a glut on the market. Many of them, since eleven hundred had been built for the military, were C-54's. The others were largely C-47's, now being slowly returned, like the DC-4's, to their peacetime designations and pursuits.

Douglas had, in the -4, managed to top its own creation. By

1946, most of the airlines had gone over to buying the big four-engined job. The reason was easy to see: the larger planes cruised at a third more speed than their smaller sister and had a carrying capacity from 55 to 70 people as opposed to the top capacity of 28 for the DC-3. The former had tricycle landing gear with steerable nose wheels; power to spare; reversible pitch propellers to aid the brakes; and a range of 2,900 miles, flying over the weather at altitudes of about 12,000 feet.

What DC-4's were left at the surplus sales, the new crop of nonscheduled "gypsy carriers" snapped up. The government prices were absurdly low—in some cases, $10,000 bought a $200,000 plane in good condition. The government itself had abruptly cancelled all orders on VJ-Day with the exception of some small experimental work.

What it meant, of course, for Douglas was that only seventy-four new DC-4's were sold at the war's end. The most famous manufacturer of commercial transport had made a profit of only one half of 1 per cent during the war years. The handwriting of red ink on the hangar walls was clear. Douglas, a man who made it a policy never to let an employee go if he could help it, had to make a decision. The irony of it was that it was not really his own: he was operating six huge plants that were 95 per cent owned by the United States government, that the government chose to shut down. But it was up to Douglas to make the decision and he made it fast and tough.

In one week, he fired 90,000 workers.

5

At this low point the traditional Douglas insistence that his planes should be a generic product paid off. He had made each one a species of legitimate flying laboratory whose mistakes and triumphs would become the palpable future. As Raymond put it, "In many respects, the DC-6 is to the DC-4 as the DC-3 is to the DC-2." The mutation of the plane line was going on undisturbed.

"Making a real mistake, as long as it isn't fatal," said one Douglas engineer, "is a whole aeronautical education in a nutshell."

From the files of what was good and bad, Douglas ferreted out the best and changed the worst. He still had 19,000 people as a skeleton force in his plants. He produced the DC-6 in February, 1946. It was put into commercial service in November the same year. New engines—the Pratt & Whitney R-2800—gave it a total thrust of 8,400 horsepower. These were tied to a fuselage that showed marked increases in strength, space, cleanness of design, and passenger appeal. Together these gave efficiency, simplicity, and economy of operation. It put new standards into the sky. The DC-6 immediately became the favorite of the airlines.

The cruising speed was lifted from 240 to 315 miles per hour. The payload rose from 11,000 to 14,000 pounds; the range jumped slightly; and the plane itself could move along at an altitude of 20,000 feet, lifting an empty weight of 51,000 pounds or a gross weight of 93,200 pounds. The big planes, filled with from 50 to 70 passengers and their baggage, mail and cargo, started off slowly as the labor force built up and the assembly lines were renovated.

They had not got to the heavens by the primrose path. Douglas had long ago committed his company's remaining assets to a jump into a region where planes (except for the military) had never flown before. Nor was it now altogether his company: in 1928, to gain financing in his difficult days, he had thrown it open to the public as a corporation with 600,000 shares of stock. Yet he still had to bear the burden of the decisions. He had made this one on his own. How to carry more passengers faster and safer and cheaper to their destination—the answer was plain. Such planes must operate at altitudes where the oft-damned air resistance was much thinner.

Douglas engineers proceeded to devise a cabin that would not explode from being pressurized within at the level of lower flight (5,000 feet as against 20,000 feet). They created superchargers that could pump in the thin outside air, sometimes as much as 70 degrees below zero, and heat it to its opposite number on the top of the thermometer. Insulating problems were solved to enable the body of the plane to resist this same frigid outside. Windows were thickened and double-paned to render them safe. The pilot was surrounded with devices to insure his responses and his own safety.

"While performance improvements," said Raymond, "plus the accompanying improved economy, would no doubt have in themselves made the DC-6 a success, this design . . . offered cabin altitude control." He believes that in air-transport history this "may well be considered the outstanding achievement of the 1940's."

6

The DC-6 was advertised as the first "entirely new" postwar plane. It had separate lounges for men and women, radiant heating, and surprising speed. It made its maiden flight to New York in 6 hours and 47 minutes. In 1948, 149 of this type had been ordered; two years later there were 200 in the lanes of seventeen different airlines, and the model was flying 360,000 miles daily. By 1952, it was calculated that every twenty-four hours the DC-6's flew the equivalent of twenty-four times around the world.

In 1952, a DC-6 made the first flight over the North Pole; and the same year another carried a record number of ninety-two passengers from New York to London. Twenty-four foreign airlines bought it. In 1953, it made a record nonstop flight of 5,700 miles in 20 hours and 30 minutes and made the first scheduled commercial round-the-world trip in a flying time of 83 hours and 4 minutes.

These developments were made possible largely by the Douglas engineers who, true to the Scots tradition of squeezing all they could out of a creation, were stretching the length, pushing the power, and pulling the wings. The DC-6A (a cargo version) was flown in September, 1949; the DC-6B took off in February, 1951. This latter became the most efficient piston-engine carrier in aviation history. In 1951, the DC-6A carried the largest single piece of freight up to that time, a 23,000-pound extrusion press, from Philadelphia to Los Angeles.

By 1957, ten years after its introduction to the air, the DC-6 planes numbered six hundred on forty-four airlines and in the military services. With one hundred more on order, this represented a bulging total of a $700,000,000 airline investment. The planes had flown nearly 88 billion miles—enough to carry all the inhabitants of New York City to London and back. It was replacing the DC-3, which by this time could only boast an average of from four to five hours in the air as against the eight hours of the average DC-6. One DC-6, over a period of two years, averaged fifteen hours daily in the air. Even a super-cautious Ethiopian airline bought two in 1958.

<h1 style="text-align:center">7</h1>

Not that the DC-6 was without faults. As a matter of fact, an original defect brought about one of the most severe crises in the history of Douglas plane manufacture.

Nearly a year after the plane was officially certified and commenced flying, in October, 1947, a United Air Lines DC-6 was cruising in routine flight over Bryce Canyon in Utah. Suddenly, to the horror of observers, the plane broke into flames. It crashed, and the fifty-two people aboard died in the wreckage.

Instantly on receipt of the report, Douglas personally demanded to know what had happened. Investigators swarmed over the spot, gathering up every possible bit of wreckage. The pieces were shipped back to Douglas. There, in a semisecret room, they were carefully put together. It became a vast skeleton of a murdered plane, scorched and melted, the pieces suspended from strings from the ceiling and laid out in a rough facsimile of the doomed airliner. It was the first such scientific reconstruction of the scene of an air disaster. The results were negligible except for one fact: the plane had caught fire in the air from a blaze apparently resulting from some source in the lower fuselage.

Nothing could be discovered that was a result of normal flying procedures. More than a hundred possible changes were brought up. The Douglas experts issued the strictest warnings to the pilots to be on the alert for any indications of fire. They had not long to wait. An American DC-6 radioed in that it had an incipient fire in its belly. It was coming in for an emergency landing at Gallup, New Mexico. Douglas men were rushed to the spot, together with government and airline experts. All DC-6's were grounded and stayed down for five months. As soon as the fire was extinguished, the DC-6 was roped off. No one was allowed near. Swarms of investigators crawled all over the plane, peering into every cranny. What they found was almost by accident.

It was routine to photograph every tiny bit of such an endangered aircraft. It was while studying enlargements of these photographs that the clue became apparent. One of the fuel-tank transfer switches was on. It meant that the pilot had not turned off the fuel as it poured from one tank to another. It was not recommended procedure, but Douglas had not specifically barred it.

It was a slight clue, but it gave the solution after an exhaustive investigation. The theory was that the fuel-tank vent—a necessary adjunct—located on the bottom of the wing was the culprit. When the stopcock was not turned off in fuel transfer, the wing tank overflowed. Fuel dripped from the vent. The slipstream caught the fuel and whisked it under the belly of the plane—directly into the mouth of a heater.

A special DC-6 was sent up to prove the theory. The tanks in question were loaded with dyed fluid to simulate gasoline. It was found that the theory was exactly right. The post-wing drip constituted a deadly hazard. It was instantly corrected: the heater and air scoops were placed ahead of the wing. The fuel vent was moved out to the very tip of the wing. Pilot procedures were changed (20 per cent had not been turning off the fuel). Since that time the DC-6 has flown without serious incident due to its construction.

As an earnest of how safe the DC-6 came to be deemed, it is enough to say that it was officially selected as the soundest plane in the air. Of the eight original purchasers, eight rebought the DC-6, and a couple came back for more as many as three times. The DC-4 had served as the original Presidential plane for President Franklin D. Roosevelt. Harry Truman used the DC-6.

8

The emergence of the DC-6 from the design board to the production line was timed with unusual precision. Douglas has always been famous for these intuitive bits of prescience. Now he demonstrated that he had not lost his touch. In the four years from 1948 to 1952, the domestic passenger-miles flown in the United States alone rose from six billion to a fantastic thirteen billion miles. The world figures of passenger flight became roughly double these figures. This doubling and redoubling meant—both to the airlines and the manufacturers—that an explosion of air travel was imminent.

They were not wrong. Somehow, in the twenty years between the numbness of 1928 and the cluttered skies in 1948, the public had caught on. Travel in the air (with its accompanying cargo) had become not only safe, fast, and economical; it had started to put on the trappings of luxury. A man could not only be as safe in a DC-6 as he would in his front parlor, he could also be situated in an environment that in most cases was far more comfortable, where his whims were catered to, his inner man fed, and his outer ego caressed. Planes, as one pilot wryly said, were being taken away from the fliers and given back to the people.

Since the DC-6 had sprung directly from the revised inspiration of the DC-4 (C-54), the airlines found few bugs after the major single defect had been nailed. Economy and efficiency of operation proved all that Douglas claimed. The demands for repair and overhaul decreased. Much to the surprise of the operators, the public actually commenced to share the pleasure of the aeronautical engineers in the clean lines and other esoteric aspects of flight. This sort of hobby had been responsible for the continuing love affair of the common man with the automobile. Now, it appeared, the same affection was beginning to blossom with the airplane.

Douglas did not neglect the booming demands of the express-freight business. There were enough improvements in engine research to justify the modest expansions of the plane to the familiar DC-6A version and the passenger DC-6B, both of which were snapped up by buying airlines for their advantages in speed, range, and payload. It was the old description of Douglas all over again: "A man with his head in the clouds, his feet on the ground, and his hand in his pocket, counting the pennies."

9

The extrusion of the spirit in wood and steel is a task generally left to the artist. In such work the individual may devote close personal attention to every detail; he may indulge his personal fancies; and he may or may not, at last, laboriously produce a single object that is unique in its beauty. He need not pay attention to public opinion or the "price" of his production. He may become famous, as has happened, without a single one of his creations being sold.

Yet the creation of the successive airplanes of Douglas has had all the qualities of art. He had not only to distill these requirements of beauty and usefulness into scientific laws, he had to do it ten thousand times over for a single model—yet with public approval and at a going price. He had, moreover, to give them that sort of enduring permanence under the roughest kind of use which is associated generally only with the eternal things of art. He had to make them economical to use and beautiful to see. All this had to be done with the identical articles that an artist might use: wires finer than human hairs, lines that would rival those of Praxiteles, aluminum alloys thinner than pages of parchment, a combined structural strength like that of an arched Roman bridge. There is scarcely any component of art that cannot be found in a great airplane.

Nor are the tests of art wanting in such a plane. The question of beauty can be answered by a single photograph, one that includes the DC-3, the DC-4, and the DC-6 and DC-7 in a single line. The proud kinship is there. As the successive models rise from their angle to the ground to flatten out and lengthen, each possesses a distinction that belongs only to works of art.

The question as to their usefulness—which means as much to Douglas (and perhaps more)—was answered by a survey in 1956. At that time it was found that the original DC-3 which sold for $110,000 brought as much as $124,000 in the open market. A DC-4 sold to the original customers for $425,000 got a price of $800,000. A new DC-6, which may have cost anywhere from $600,000 to $900,000, could not be bought then for less than $1,400,000. The DC-6B, which originally cost between $1,000,-000 and $1,500,000, was worth nearly $2,000,000 as a used aircraft. It was a seller's market based on the best piston-engine aircraft ever built. It was to collapse upon the advent of the demand for jet transports, but in those years it was unique.

10

One of the most difficult tasks in modern life is to offer and maintain a scheme of personal integrity in terms of mechanical achievement. Too often the machine takes over the personality. The character defers to the crisis, the intangible to the inanimate. In few other industries does this become more apparent than in building an airplane, a machine that must achieve the trust of the world (nearly sixty nations fly original Douglas planes or direct imitations of them) in boosting man upward to an alien and hostile environment. In the discharge of this responsibility, Douglas saw that its design was nearing the end of the line—at least as far as the second grouping of planes was concerned, the "family" that had begun with the DC-4.

Raymond had expressed much earlier the Douglas principle that aircraft must evolve in a sound, orderly fashion rather than in a dramatic upsweep. Now, as usual, the end of one rootstock was in sight. New power plants—the turbojet, the pure jet, the rocket, and even the ramjet and atomic-energy engines—were in the first stages of being perfected for commercial use. If in 1940 the Douglas transports had made up more than 90 per cent of the world's scheduled airline-route miles, in 1953 they had fallen to something above 80 per cent. Hundreds of DC-4's and DC-3's were still flying—the British European Airways even equipped the old DC-3 with new turboprop power—but the DC-6 was the supreme instrument of passenger-mile profits. It was flying more than 500,000 miles daily and was beginning to justify its total production cost of $38,000,000. It had amply justified the faith of five major airlines, which, in 1944—before the design of the DC-6 had actually been finished on paper—ordered $50,000,000 worth.

But the signs were plain. It was time for Douglas to get off this particular design, to develop a new one without sacrificing any of the advantages of the old. The question—one of the most serious questions in Douglas history—was how far and how fast to move ahead.

"It was obvious, by this time," said Raymond, "that the military effort in engine development was moving rapidly from piston to jet, and the big question was: When will the jet offer commercial reliability?

"While a number of possible engine-airframe combinations were being explored, the Wright company came up with the turbocompound 3350, probably the most efficient large piston engine ever to be developed."

It was instantly obvious that merely replacing the old engines in the DC-6 airframe would produce an increased range and payload. It would also give an upping of speed that would be comparable to the advance of the DC-6 over the DC-4. This meant that for the first time the advertising and publicity departments of Douglas would be able to play with the idea of commercial non-stop cross-country schedules. It was a prospect that was highly appealing. In the end, it won the day. "After much soul searching, plus some powerful urging by the able president of American Airlines, we decided that the timing of the jet-engine picture allowed an adequate period for development and use of the airplane which we know as the DC-7," Raymond added.

11

"God, how I envy that name!" cried a vice-president of a competing airline when he heard of the DC-7C "Seven Seas" airliner. It was a natural reaction: the obvious nickname packed all the romance of the past into a package. His envy was not only for the title but for the plane itself.

The DC-7C was the last model of its family. It ended the procession of 24 miles of planes, 1,000 DC-6's, DC-7's, and DC-7C's worth $1,300,000,000. The DC-7, which made its debut in November, 1953, was the foster child of American Airlines: they were the first to agree with Douglas that a new plane that could carry more people across the continent nonstop was needed. With bigger engines and more seats, it caused a sensation in the sky. American ordered enough to make production worth while. The DC-7's cost more to operate, but they were worth it.

What sold the DC-7 to Pan American for 1954 use was that airline's obsession with flying about the world. It wanted a plane that could fly the oceans either way, in any kind of weather, at comfortable heights and fast speeds, with a resounding payload of passengers. "So," said a Douglas engineer, "we stretched the DC-4 again—eight feet and from 70,000 to 140,000 pounds. We got us a new work horse." It passed through the increasing series of tests —systems, strength, model, wind-tunnel, simulation, and even "comfortization" tests—and won a place in the Douglas plane hierarchy. It made a fetish of aerodynamic cleanness: the drag of the whole plane was equal to no more than a rod two inches in diameter and about 118 feet long held crosswise in the windstream.

The DC-7 could carry from 64 to 95 passengers, and had a capacity of about 20,000 pounds of cargo. Its wing span was 117 feet (identical to DC-4's), but its length was now 109 feet. With a take-off weight of 140,000 pounds, its four engines had 13,000 horsepower. It could push above 400 miles per hour and go perhaps 4,400 miles. But it was not to escape its own searing publicity in an accident for which the plane itself was not responsible.

In January, 1957, while a test crew was making a normal test descent for landing, a DC-7B model (put out in 1955) was struck by an F-89 military fighter. The Douglas radio operator at the plant caught the last agonized words of the DC-7B pilot: "Midair collision . . . midair collision . . . 10 HOW [identification of the test plane] . . . we're going . . . uncontrollable . . . uncontrollable . . . say good-by to everybody . . ."

An official investigation cleared Douglas. The scars remained until the first flight of the DC-7C—a year after the DC-7. It boasted carved leather murals, mahogany paneling, and wall-to-wall carpeting. It had been enlarged in almost every direction, in the immemorial tradition. Ten feet more on the wings, three feet on the fuselage, two feet more on the tail—lifting 143,000 pounds and carrying from 48 to 105 passengers for 5,000 miles at rates of 400 miles per hour at 25,000 feet. Its counterpart could carry 34,600 pounds in freight at speeds coast-to-coast of 365 miles per hour. The original complaints of the deafening thunder of the engines outside had been reduced by moving the nearest engines five feet further away.

But good as the DC-7 was, and in service by the spring of 1956, it already had a rival on the drawing board. The elastic design of the DC-4 had gone as far as it could. The new plane, the DC-8, was not even to be a kissing cousin of its old relatives. It was to enter a totally new sphere of aeronautics.

FIVE:

E PLURIBUS UNUM

1

THERE IS a legend that young Douglas, while at the Naval Academy, flew a miniature model out of his window and smacked a strolling admiral on the ear. It is untrue. It is true that he sometimes forgot nails in the gymnasium floor, after he had completed some amateur tension experiments, and tripped up a squad of drilling middies.

Whatever his early contact with the military, the Douglas boot has always been one of the most welcome feet in the door ever since those days at Annapolis. He has built planes for every branch of the military service. His efforts have been extraordinarily successful. The reason for his continued position of eminence in military manufacture—although he is chiefly known as a commercial-transport man—is the unusual company combination of daring ideas with conservative building.

"A brutal way to put it," murmured one Douglas designer, "is to say that war is our experimental laboratory. Perhaps we're freer than most of that kind of raw guilt, but it's a fact that without it none of the big plane manufacturing companies could have made such long strides into the future."

In military aviation Douglas has been one of the pioneers. Not the foremost nor the first in the field, but certainly the company that has produced an imposing list of firsts in everything that flies. Plane for plane, in three wars, it has far outproduced any other company.

Making aircraft for war is not a particularly profitable enterprise. It will keep a large company afloat with a succession of orders, in design, research, and manufacture; but the profit margins are relatively small and sharply regulated. Nor can the orders be depended on. The cyclical and rightful investigations of Congress and the recurring red tape often make such contracts a nightmare.

Nevertheless, the advantages of wartime plane making are many. Techniques of assembly, new uses of materials, and the education of future customers are only a few of the benefits. Above all, any conflict always produces new sciences and new ways of advancing knowledge. Without World Wars I and II—and the cold war that threatens a World War III—aviation might very well still be languishing in the doldrums of the stick-and-canvas era.

What man has to invent, he will; what he is inspired to do, he will. But unless he is threatened, he takes his time about getting on with it. War is useful enough to the aircraft industry to be next to a necessity. Virtually every modern advance has been due, at least in execution and pace, to the demands of the impossible in aircraft.

The first Douglas orders go back to the military. After the whim of a flying sport had denied him his first order, he took the same plans back to Washington. He came back with his first three offhand inspirations of "torpedo planes." They were so successful that he got orders for thirty more. He was able at last to abandon the two-acre potato patch he was hoeing so badly, and give his time to design.

Meanwhile, the Martin bomber he had designed was flying and making new records. Rather than compete directly, Douglas went into the observation series of planes. He branched out into the M-1's and thence to his first large cargo plane, the C-1. This he abandoned, but it proved the direction he was following.

It may be said in retrospect that Douglas never deviated from his goal, even though he probably did not know it at the time. Scrounging for orders, working like a man possessed, he had no time to look ahead and decide upon an ultimate goal. But it was in the folds of his brain from the beginning.

Every Douglas model from the start is a preview in some small part of the final achievement, the giant DC-8. Douglas never revised his ideas; he merely modified or strengthened them. It is comparatively easy to see how the commercial planes gradually funneled into the building and production of the DC-8. It is not as easy to demonstrate what the military work of Douglas contributed to that end. The fact is there, imbedded in purpose and ideal from 1920 to 1960.

2

The romantically named *Cloudster*, which became the somewhat comically titled DT series, was the first plane in history (and one of the last) able to lift a useful load equivalent to its own weight. This did not represent a sporting achievement; in that respect it was a design failure. It represented a notable advance in pure levitation, a feature much more to be desired and much more in demand than a simple speed plane. The DC-8 does not do nearly that well today, but it has inherent disadvantages in its size. What it does do is roughly equivalent: it at least lifts one passenger per ton, plus mail, baggage, fuel, and sometimes cargo.

The *Cloudster*, it must be realized, was not the original Douglas design. That credit goes to his work while with Martin, in designing a purely military craft, the first big bomber. Douglas can be given credit on his own for cleaning up the lines of early military aeronautics. It used to be said that after a plane was built a pigeon was released among the maze of wires, struts, and canvas. If the bird could fly out, the plane was unsafe. Douglas had remarked that the building of planes was "99 per cent mathematics." He proved it.

Some figures may be offered in proof of the importance of the military orders to the experimental and financial development of Douglas. In 1922, Douglas built 6 planes; he sold them for $130,890. In 1929, the year of the stock-market crash, when Douglas stock was on the rise, he sold 97 for a total of $1,970,961. In 1937, the sale of 303 planes brought in $20,950,361—and the unfulfilled orders amounted to $31,000,000. Of this backlog, about $24,750,000 was owed to the Army and Navy.

Military plane making was for long years the backbone of the Douglas effort. Not until 1958, for the first time in the history of the company, did civilian commercial orders reach even half the amount of the government orders. Yet Douglas had always been interested primarily in achieving the goal of commercial transport.

The seeming contradiction—which is not really much of a one, properly understood—lies in the vastly different outlook of the armed forces from that of the general public. It is the duty of the former establishment to look ahead, to experiment, to plan, and to win the deadly competition for supremacy in the air going on in the world. Douglas and his art could not fail to be part of this struggle that in the latter years has shifted to space. As far as the aviation war in the atmosphere is concerned, Douglas and his fellow manufacturers won it long ago for the United States in military respects. Leading the skeptical American public into the air age was not as easy.

A single additional statistic will point up the difference. In 1938, the sales of Douglas craft amounted to a startling $28,000,000. Of this total, about $16,000,000 went to foreign countries. It was easier to be a prophet—and to make a profit—in other lands than one's own. Not even Douglas' own father believed him. "To an ordinary man like myself," he said long after the success of his son, "a future in aviation seemed fantastic."

3

Fantastic it was and fantastic it would have remained except for the military. "An alert and ambitious military technical personnel played its part in accelerating the use of brains by our designers," said Douglas in 1935. Five years later, with World War II begun, he had some second thoughts on military aviation and its tendencies. "I know no formulae by which to tell a defensive airplane from one used in offense. Our tables deal with mathematics, not motives. In a world so full of conflict and confusion, the greatest discoveries and gifts of science become slaves and servants, not always on the side of right and justice. The laws of gravity and aerodynamics recognize no distinctions between aggressor and victim. The dictator and the defender share alike in the triumphs of science."

Despite his doubts, Douglas and his co-workers were fundamentally sustained by their duty as Americans and their faith in the ultimate vindication of aeronautics as an instrument of civilization rather than of destruction. In 1932, three years before he praised the military spur to dominance of the sky, he had established a new aircraft division in an abandoned 20,000-square-foot building in El Segundo, California. Here, with fifteen experienced plane builders, he inaugurated what was to become the chief military production plant.

The first ship built was the Gamma-Skychief. With Hawks at the controls, this custom-built racer with its oddly faired wheels created several transcontinental records. The next product, the Gamma-Polar Star, went into the Antarctic with Lincoln Ellsworth, the famous explorer, as pilot. It has ended its flying days in the museum of the Smithsonian Institution.

The first fighting plane created was the XFT fighter for the Navy in 1933. The same year, the Model 2C for the A-17 (or attack bomber) series for the Army Air Corps was produced. It was a highly successful prototype, first of a long series. For years its design became standard for such bombers. It was followed by the BT-1 in 1934, a dive bomber that was the legitimate father of the famous SBD Dauntless dive bomber used in World War II.

It can be noted here that the SBD's—which went into production luckily in June, 1940, about eighteen months before Pearl Harbor —brought the first Congressional Medal of Honor to the Marine

Corps and its aviation branch. The medal was posthumously awarded to Captain Richard E. Fleming, USMC. The young pilot, his sturdy plane riddled with antiaircraft fire and bursting into flames, managed to hold a direct dive on a Japanese battleship. His plane held together long enough in that historic battle of Midway Island to plunge directly into the vitals of the ship after releasing its bomb. It was this same plane that was used again and again by the Navy and Marine Corps—in 5,991 improved copies— throughout the war. It was praised by Secretary of the Navy James Forrestal as "probably the most destructive single weapon in the Navy's arsenal." New combat needs produced the SBD-2, -3, -4, -5, and -6.

The A-20 attack plane for the Army came through in 1939. It achieved a similar reputation. A total of 7,486 of these were built for the Army (and the French and British), some as the DB-7 Boston. The military orders commenced to pour in, and the DC-5 commercial transport had to be dropped (not without a Douglas sigh of relief) to take on the demands of the fight in the air.

The original SBD proved to be the best of them all. One wartime account told of its prowess: "It has no bugs, no streaks of temperament, a thoroughly honest aircraft. It could take a frightful beating and stagger home on wings that sometimes looked like nutmeg graters. . . . Its loss ratio was the lowest of all United States carrier aircraft in the Pacific." And, indeed, in 1944, the SBD was credited with sinking more combatant tonnage than all other arms of the Navy. Even the Army took 170 of the same craft, disguising them under the title of A-24's.

4

The performance of the SBD overshadowed that of its sister Douglas creations. The A-26 Invader was a sample—a versatile prototype that could be used as a fighter, bomber, night fighter, strafer, even as a torpedo bomber. Still other models, such as the SB2D-1 Destroyer, were designed but not produced because of the rapidly changing demands of tactics. It was redesigned in 1944 as the BT2D-1 and then changed in name only to the AD-1 Skyraider, which saw Korean service. Another model in 1945, the TB2D-Skypirate, never got into the fight because of the early Japanese surrender.

The collapse of World War II heralded a similar collapse of the Douglas effort. The virtually total cancellation of contracts (only one small contract for the AD-1 remained with the plant) came close to bankrupting all involved. The company saved itself by mass firings and the abrupt halting of assembly lines. Bitter about the lack of continuity in military orders—something that not even the naturally pessimistic Douglas had expected as a reward for his extraordinary services—the engineers frantically cast about for new fields in aviation. Although 3,180 of the AD's were to be sold, no one could then foresee it. No one could guess it would establish the longest continuous deliveries of any military airplane then in production with its twenty-eight different model designations. As the "work horse of the fleet," the improved AD set a world's record in May, 1953, by carrying a bomb load of 10,500 pounds. It was significant for the commercial developments of the future.

In 1945, only a few visualized the advances of the new era in aviation. "The future is as dark as the inside of a boot," growled Douglas. He had a right to his view. His plants were empty; his engineers were lean and hungry. He himself was scrabbling for business. He was happy when his company got the first of a series of comparatively small orders on the D-558 National Research Project. It produced a first-phase airplane, the famous Skystreak—a thin-winged, jet-propelled experiment for the Navy in collaboration with the National Advisory Committee for Aeronautics.

Less than twenty-three months later, the engineers at Douglas saw their imaginative product—it looked like a bit of bamboo transfixed by a knife blade—hit the sky. It was a unique craft. It broke the world speed record by flying 640.7 miles per hour; and then, five days later, it cracked it again by flying 650.6 miles per hour. Nor was its brother, the D-558-2 Skyrocket, any less famous. As the phase-two craft of the program, the latter was the first airplane to fly twice the speed of sound after its first flight in February, 1948. In November, 1953, it flew 1,327 miles per hour. And, to top it all, the needle-nosed little ship held the world's altitude record of 83,235 feet until mid-1954.

These planes had been designed largely to investigate in level flight the aerodynamic problems met by other, less speedy planes in dives. The data gathered made even faster planes possible, but that was not their real significance. The data collected from *all* the Douglas experiments, paid for from whatever source, was beginning to pile up. Within this greenhouse of data was growing the seed of the super-transports of the future.

5

Take the load-carrying ability of the Skyraider. Plus the speed of the Skystreak. Plus the advances of the Skyrocket both in speed and in altitude. They prefigure the shape of the commercial airliner of the future: dark, shadowy, and with numberless question marks, but rousing the cohering vision of the Douglas designers and engineers. The Navy-NACA money and their own talents had produced the blueprint of what was to come.

Nor was the culminating effort lost to the military. It was largely involved in the F3D Skyknight, whose preliminary design was on the boards only shortly after that of the Skystreak. It was a two-place jet fighter, a black knight with stubby wings and a curiously shaped tail. It went into full production with the outbreak of the Korean War. It became the world's first jet to shoot down another jet in night combat. It went on to become the Navy's best in its field, leading all others in the total number of night kills. Another design, the XA2D Skyshark, never went into production. It used counter-rotating propellers driven by two jet engines to combine the "possible best" of both worlds of power. It failed. Faster, pure jets were on the line.

It was clear that jet power was taking over the sky. All sorts of experiments had been tried with piston engines and had failed. The propellers, once the pilot's best friends, were now his worst enemy in their limitations of speed. When the Korean affair broke in June, 1950, the indecisive aircraft industry—torn between new designs and power plants—was producing only 215 aircraft. Another lesson on the book: the ballooning of a business, only to be popped by the cut-off of military orders, was not healthy.

In February, 1955, the Navy's Skyray (F4D)—a supersonic interceptor—added its own primer to the pile of Douglas lessons. It shot from a standing start into the air, rising to 10,000 feet in 56 seconds. It took official military records up another peg by establishing an average of 3-kilometer speed of 752.9 miles per hour and a 100-kilometer speed of 728.1 miles per hour. The midget A4D Skyhawk of 1955 with its delta-wing configuration took the 500-kilometer official record at 695.1 miles per hour. It was matched with the big A3D Skywarrior, which had appeared in 1952 as a 70,000-pound sophisticated Pegasus of new abilities. Last of all came the F5D Skylancer, produced in 1956, with a thin delta wing and a long needle fuselage.

Douglas now had the know-how of high flying, of speed, of configuration, of load carrying, and of the eccentricities of jet power. The aeronautical facts were driving the company relentlessly to the development of the DC-8. What was desired was some sort of broad experimental vehicle on which they could test some of the combined fact and theory that lay on their desks. The opportunity had appeared with the building of the C-74, the C-124 Globemaster, and the C-133 Cargomaster.

6

The C-74 of 1947 was the first big Douglas cargo plane. It grossed a weight of 172,000 pounds and was independent of ground facilities. It had self-contained power units to allow its crews to change engines, operate a belly freight elevator, and handle small electrical cranes and cargo belts. Thirteen of these were delivered in the initial order. Immediately it was obvious that a new version to carry more than 30,000 pounds, with a minimum increase in gross weight, was needed.

The C-124 was designed as the answer. It was manufactured in 1949, flying for the first time in November. It was delivered to the United States Air Force in May, 1950, for use in the Korean War. In the period from 1950 to 1956, these massive planes were used so extensively that they logged nearly a million flying hours, covering a distance equal to a trip to the sun and back, or around the world eight thousand times. These trips were made over every kind of terrain in existence, under all sorts of weather conditions, and with payloads of 50,000 pounds carried 2,000 miles without refueling. Range was squeezed up to 500 miles more. The payload, on shorter trips, shot up to 70,000 pounds.

This bulky, low-winged airplane, without grace or majesty, was one of the most-needed airplanes of its day. It eventually came to be a part of virtually all the services that flew. It operated at both the North and South Poles. It was designed to stand temperatures as low as 70 degrees below zero and 200 degrees above. Its cargo cabin was famous for its 10,000 cubic feet of space, which could carry 94 per cent of all military vehicles in an assembled condition; or 200 fully armed combat troops; or 127 litter patients with the necessary doctors and nurses. Among other innovations, it had a clamshell nose door that allowed a built-in ramp to be extended for quick loading. As a corollary, it had an elevator in the middle that could quickly unload at the same time. Its wing span of 174 feet and its length of 130 feet, together with its 48-foot height, made it seem unwieldy and stubby, but it handled perfectly in the air. It was joined in due time by its bigger brother, the C-133; the last C-124 was handed over to the military in May, 1955.

This giant transport, urgently requested by the service as a logistic development that could carry troops and weapons to any point on the globe in the fastest possible time, flew for the Air Force for the first time in August, 1957. Its capabilities of lift became clear when in December, 1958, working for the Military Air Transport Service, a C-133 lifted a record-breaking 117,900 pounds into the air—more than 26,000 pounds over its approved maximum payload in design.

How important this was to the military organization of the United States is best shown by a series of feats achieved by the high-winged C-133. Used by MATS, a service that makes two thousand flights monthly over more than 115,000 miles of water routes, the C-133 achieved some extraordinary records. It was able to carry the gigantic Atlas missile, fully assembled. It was capable of exceeding the C-124 record of carrying an entire fighter squadron, including the supersonic F-104 jet planes. Its 13,000 feet of cargo space allowed it to lift twice the load of the C-124 and to do it with less expense per ton mile. Sixteen fully loaded jeeps or two 40,000-pound earth movers proved to be no obstacle to C-133 power.

In brushfire scares such as the 1958 shelling of Quemoy off Formosa and the American aid sent into Lebanon at the height of the crisis there in the same year, the C-124's had proved their own integrity of performance. "Adequate military airlift is vital to America's national security," Eisenhower had declared. The C-133 was the answer to the implied question of the President.

It was no less vital to the future of the Douglas company, which had designed the biggest cargo planes in the world. It was no accident that they flew above 320 miles an hour and had un-excelled safety and maintenance records. There had been proved savings. Five typical items, selected from the Army inventory list, were surveyed for air-transportation costs. It was demonstrated that airlifting an office desk saved $15.10; airlifting a liquid-oxygen tank instead of sending it by any other transportation means saved as much as $376.73. Douglas was not only impressed by this but by the fact that only about 4 per cent of the total of 16,000,000 tons annually shipped overseas to American defense bases was sent by air. There must be, the company reasoned, a huge market for cargo as well as passengers.

They stretched the C-133 again in the traditional Douglas

manner. In a sense the high-wing C-133 was a design throwback to the early flying boats of Douglas which appeared in the 1930's. The hulking, clean-lined YOA, with its two engines mounted above, and the later Dolphin were two of the best known. They had much the same high wing with engines above, which was not to prove efficient until the advent of the C-133, a purely land plane. But they performed as well as their maker thought they might, and looked like no more than small boats with a plank and power units laid across the top.

The pilots found that the C-133B could carry more than 26 tons for a distance of 4,000 miles at an average speed of 323 miles per hour—for a cost of about six cents per ton a mile. It was clear that out of the cocoon of military expectations and demands was to come the commercial victory represented by the DC-8.

7

Because of the kissin'-cousin relationship of all Douglas creations for the air, it is important to consider its latest and possibly most significant work for the military. It lies in the field of missiles. These have, of course, not been in the direct line of the production of the DC-8. But the missile work has produced notable research products that have combined their airborne assets into that highly respected carrier.

The manufacture of missiles at Douglas is a surprisingly long history. Its first samples were put together in 1941, at approximately the same time that the Nazi German production of its own V-1's—the first really modern missile force established in the world —was moving ahead. By the end of 1958, the company had produced 19,000 missiles; by the end of the next year, more than 30,000; and by the end of 1960, an estimated 55,000. It was a series covering all four basic missile categories of air-to-surface, air-to-air, surface-to-air, and surface-to-surface. Production contracts were executed for Army, Navy, and Air Force demands. Some of these were the Navy's air-to-air Sparrow, the Air Force's

air-to-air Genie with an atomic warhead, the Air Force's Thor intermediate ballistic missile, and the Army's surface-to-air Nike-Ajax
and Hercules.

The beginnings of an effective anti-missile system were due in
large measure to Douglas. The production of the first such defense
weapon was begun in 1957 in association with the Bell Telephone
and Western Electric laboratories.

The outstanding success of Douglas in the missile field was the
Thor intermediate-range ballistic missile. A 1,500-to-2,000-mile
weapon, it was developed in thirteen months. Models were successfully tested and production lines set in operation to turn them out to
almost any degree that might be necessary. In addition to the
manufacture of this intermediate missile, Douglas also designed,
tested, and built the tactical system required for its operations.

Douglas found that he himself had to be very frank about government red tape and its interference in his company's work. In
his testimony before the Senate Armed Services Subcommittee on
Preparedness, in January, 1958, Douglas said: "One conspicuous
example of failure to make early and firm decisions in the government is the Zeus anti-missile project. Nearly two years ago [in 1956]
we felt this weapon was sufficiently feasible to warrant a go-ahead.
But so far only a small fraction of the necessary funds has been
made available." Douglas went on to mention that even in the case
of the Thor IRBM (after successful test firings) his company waited
from August to December for an order to increase production on
the missile.

He declared that "one service itself estimates that an average of
333 days is required to process a facilities request" and that need-
less paper work for the government forced an addition of 30 per
cent more technical manpower. Finally Douglas pointed out that
his company spent "upward of 400,000 man-hours a year" in preparing unnecessary checking and reports.

At this same hearing Douglas declared that one of the "woeful
lacks in our defense planning" was that there was not sufficient
modern cargo aircraft available to lift troops and supplies to the

points where they might be needed for combat. He said, "The C-130 [Lockheed] and the C-133, the only modern and efficient cargo aircraft of this type in our inventory, are being acquired at a painfully slow rate." This seemed an obvious plea for a grant to Douglas to build more such planes. Despite the business aspects of his statement, the facts he brought out represented a fair summary of a serious problem.

Douglas was aware that aviation was coming of age in a commercial rather than a military sense. The hazards of any government contract were steadily being increased. He felt, unless war intervened, that private industry must come to represent the true potential of his business of building planes.

SIX:

WHERE ARE WE NOW?

1

IT WAS a dull afternoon in the depths of the depression years. The future of the business of flight seemed as dim as the fogged Santa Monica weather outside. The inspired, definitive design of the DC-1 had not yet been thought of.

That was the day Douglas called his little squad of designers into his office. He stared at them under his shaggy brows and said gently, "I want you to design a plane wing modeled after the buzzard's wing."

His staff blinked. "I want work to start right away," Douglas continued in his deceptively mild voice, which they knew could rouse in an instant to a storm of denunciation. He went on to say why he wanted it.

He told of how a buzzard could gorge almost twice its weight, yet take off in a short run and soar upward almost without wing motion. "Maximum payload at minimum cost," said Douglas, "and practically no runway." He described the simplicity of the buzzard's skeletal construction and praised it. "Remarkable basic design," he said. He related how far the buzzard could soar, hour after hour, with no apparent effort. "Maximum fuel economy," he explained.

Finally, he whipped out a stuffed buzzard and held it dramatically aloft before his gaping audience. He turned on an electric fan and slowly extended the wing before the breeze. "Notice the camber," he said admiringly. "Did you ever see such a lift ratio per square inch of wing surface?"

He put the buzzard down and his face hardened. He waved them out. "Get busy and design," he ordered.

The designers filed out, their faces a study in bewilderment. For the next two weeks they slaved over their drawing boards before they found the scientific proof that Douglas was playing one of his famous practical jokes.

"What he was asking for," said one of them afterward, "was really wooden feathers. But we never questioned what he said. The Old Man was a top aeronautical engineer himself."

Douglas had done what he wanted to do. He had got his idle staff busy on a project; he had jolted their imaginations. By the time the 1932 "birth certificate" of the DC-1 came through—the letter from Frye—he had the minds of his assistants tooled up to do the job.

Not many of the aeronautical engineers and designers at Douglas are bird watchers. Few of them have studied intensively the flight of a bird, one of the great mysteries of nature. As Dr. Wesley Lanyon, of the American Museum of Natural History, points out, "The wing of an airplane is far less complex than a bird's flexible, jointed, magnificent wing."

Such study has never been needed: manmade airplanes work on an entirely different principle from bird-made flight. In their own field, they have become much more successful than birds. But the concept of an airplane, like that of the development of birds, remains evolutionary. It issues originally from the deep wells of intuition, training, and experience. It is refined by stages of humbling experiment and often, even then, the result is to a degree unpredictable. What is needed is the maturing of an idea by the passing of time, a process that no one can hurry.

2

The concept of the DC-8 stands alone. It is both the latest and last infant of the DC line of airplanes and the most ancient patriarch. On the Douglas genealogical chart, virtually every type of plane ever invented converges to produce the DC-8. Some detail or refinement of a fighter, bomber, reconnaissance, amphibian, sports, racer, cargo, or passenger plane contributed to it. But only seven models make up the direct ancestry of the DC-8. No one will be surprised at the prosaic numbering that runs for fewer than ten major predecessors. They are grouped into three families: the DC-1, -2, -3, and the abortive -5, all of them twin-motors; the massive DC-4, -6, and -7 series of four engines; and, finally, all by itself, the DC-8.

This succession of airplanes—which has had unsuccessful cousins within the family tree—was not harebrained into being by some genius of a designer doodling on his own. It was rather a community of concepts. In the traditional Douglas fashion, everyone connected with a new project—and even some outsiders with weird extrapolations—came up with his notions. On these was exerted the solidifying and concentrating force of what could be done in the light of the technology that existed. "We were forced to certain conclusions at each step simply by aeronautical and economic laws," said Raymond soberly. "As an example, the Boeing 707 and the DC-8 do have strong points of resemblance. Outsiders have accused one and then the other of 'stealing' various angles of design. Actually, in competition with everyone striving for roughly the same goals in the same field, the best results can't help but resemble each other."

If there is any way to break the laws of the air, Douglas and any other plane manufacturer would be glad to steal a march on a competitor. But the code of flight must be bent gently before it is snapped into a new statute. This takes years of investigation and effort, and a multitude of decisions.

3

The first glimmering of the DC-8 goes back as far as 1937. At that time Douglas began to design the first intercontinental bomber in the world for the United States Air Force. It was called the B-19.

The B-19, which never flew in anger during the war, was the biggest bomber of the world in its day. Built in 1941 and flown in June of that year, it was used as a flying laboratory, with its wing-spread of 212 feet (bigger than the DC-8), a bomb payload of 18 tons, and a range of nearly 8,000 miles. It was one of a kind, a lesson for the manufacturer. It was ten years before its day. Its lessons in prototype were learned by the B-36. Its building and testing turned the World War II idea toward the smaller B-17 and B-24. Later, the Air Matériel Command used the lattice-nosed B-19 to test out ideas that Boeing put into the B-29 and the version of the B-29 that was the B-50.

The B-19 did not do too much to antedate the modern Eight, but it did prove to the satisfaction of Douglas that the wing could lift a big body and great weights. It had innate possibilities of being refined to achieve great speeds.

The second candle that must be held up to the achievement of the Eight was the XB-43 of 1945. This was a very small bomber, with a cocked tail like a rooster's. It was too late for it to be really of any use to the military. But it proved invaluable, like the B-19, as a flying laboratory. It was the historic plane that carried, buried in its fuselage, the first two reliably operable jet engines made by General Electric. The Air Force got a good deal of use out of the XB-43 before they discarded it.

A third experimental plane should be mentioned briefly. For almost nine years, from 1943 to 1952, the futuristic minds at Douglas lovingly fiddled with an experimental plane called the X-3. It was a dart-pointed, tiny-winged thing with twin cannon of jet engines. It was designed to probe further into the sound and heat barriers already explored by the Skystreak and Skyrocket, but its chief use was an investigation into titanium. Built largely of this light but difficult and expensive metal, the X-3 gave the Douglas metallurgists and engineers a chance to pioneer techniques of working and handling and forming. During its gestation the X-3 also managed to become, as Raymond put it, "one of the really important progenitors of the F-100 series of supersonic fighters." Research on the wings, nose, and tail of the X-3 was measurably helpful in arriving at the later and more conservative design of the Eight.

The first real studies for the DC-8 power plant may be dated back to 1945. They commenced, as such studies always do, with an intensive examination and evaluation of the available engines. In those years jet engines certainly existed and operated, as had been proved by their successful use in World War II. However, they had enormous fuel consumption and to a large degree were unreliable. Worse than that, they lacked the necessary thrust to become an accessory to commercial transports. It was not until 1951, when the Pratt & Whitney JT3 engine was to appear—a commercial improvement over the military J57 engine—that any of the airplane manufacturers could take commercial jet travel seriously.

The proved characteristics of the B-19 and the XB-43, added to the probable jet-engine improvement, were invaluable to the Douglas engineers. "We were no longer surprised that a big plane could fly," said Ivar Shogran, chief project engineer for the DC-8. Nor were they surprised that they could build a giant airframe to match their ideas. As late as 1955, they made a $400,000 proposal to the Air Force for a giant jet bomber. The design, including many of the features that were later to be included in the Eight, won the competition from all comers, but the Douglas plane never flew. It was a pure jet. The order stayed with Boeing.

For the inexorable reasons of commercial survival, the Douglas designers were driven on to the first inklings of the commercial giant of jet transport. They had to win in a market that was already leaning away from them in military orders. They had satisfied

Roll-out of the first DC-8 following a special ceremony.

The DC-8 comes in for a landing at Baltimore after its first transcontinental flight. (*Wide World Photo*)

It all began in the back room of this barbershop (1920).

Skilled hands build a World Cruiser fuselage in Wilshire Boulevard plant (early 1920's).

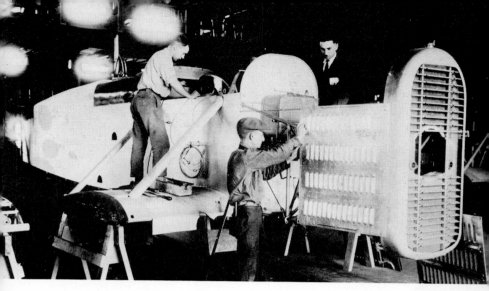

Final assembly of a DT (Douglas Torpedo) plane built for the Navy.
Donald W. Douglas, Sr., in dark suit (1921–24).

Women employees cover the fuselage of a World Cruiser (1924).

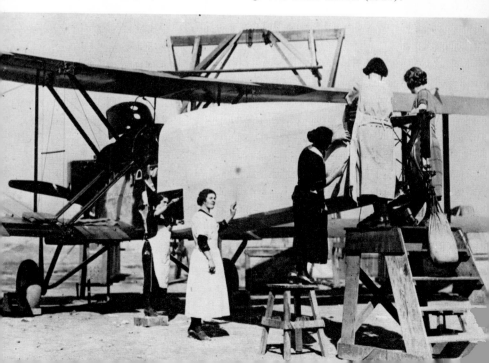

The *Cloudster*.

Douglas 'Round-the-World Cruiser.

The DC-1, first of the "DC" (Douglas Commercial) series.

The DC-2.

The DC-3 at one time carried 95 per cent of all commercial traffic.

The DC-4: the "perfect" transport plane.

The DC-6.

The DC-7 made possible nonstop flights across the United States.

The DC-7C "Seven Seas," so named because it can span any body of water in the world.

A Douglas C-124 Globemaster en route to the South Pole.

themselves, on paper at least, that in their design for the jet, which incorporated the features of the B-19 of 1937 and the XB-43 of ten years later, they had the key to their success.

4

In the summer of 1955, Peter G. Masefield, a knowledgeable British authority on commercial transport, pointed out some hard facts to the airlines of the world. He declared that there were roughly eighteen hundred four-engine transports flying on the airlines of the world, plus about as many twin-engine models. The rate of depreciation was approximately on the order of ten years. Air transport was growing annually at a rate of between 15 and 20 per cent.

Masefield mentioned that in the early 1930's the first transport revolution had come when the biplanes and trimotored planes had been replaced by planes such as the DC-2 cantilevered monoplane with retractable landing gear. The second had appeared when the big four-engine monoplanes, with pressurized cabins, had come into existence.

It was Masefield's opinion that there would be seven similar developments in the near future. The first, he said, would be the intercontinental long-range jet transport, ". . . which will have to cruise at around 550 miles per hour and carry rather more than one hundred passengers with an intercontinental time of four and a half hours." He guessed it would weigh about 150 tons and cost about six million dollars. He put the world market for such planes at about three hundred, an investment of about two billion dollars. "I hope the pocket of the airlines is long enough," he commented.

The second category Masefield brought up was the world market for about four hundred long-range turboprop planes at a cost of about one and a half billion dollars. Flying 450 miles per hour, weighing 90 tons, and costing about three and a half million dollars apiece, they would be a major outlay in themselves.

The third category of Masefield was a "70-passenger, 75-ton,

500-mile-per-hour airplane capable of flying about 2,000 miles nonstop." He felt it would sell for about two and a half million dollars and have a market of a hundred aircraft. His work-horse category was fourth: a 50-ton airplane carrying about 80 passengers with a cost of under two million dollars and cruising at more than 400 miles an hour. He envisioned a market for five hundred of these in the world.

The fifth plane in the Masefield prophecy was the secondary work horse, which would carry perhaps 50 passengers at about 350 miles per hour and weigh 35 tons. "I fancy there is a world demand for some four hundred of these airplanes at around one million dollars each," he said—a six-hundred-million-dollar free-for-all.

In category six, Masefield called for a replacement for the familiar DC-3, which had been a favorite—and still is—of every airline in the world. He said he expected a demand for a 10-ton airplane, cruising slightly under 300 miles an hour and carrying 30 passengers at a cost of about four hundred thousand dollars. He imagined there would be a demand for about six hundred of these.

In category seven he mentioned "a larger multi-engine helicopter designed to fly directly between city centers up to 250 miles apart, as well as between a few major airports." He mentioned that the studies of the industry had confirmed that the helicopter could not be a true commercial transport until it could offer 50 seats at a cruising rate of 150 miles per hour. However, he did say that if it could be produced, even at a rather expensive cost of one and a half million dollars at 30 tons gross weight, there would be room for at least five hundred of them, a market of about a billion dollars.

It was an excellent prophecy. It was one which expressed the philosophy of a great many airlines and which to a major degree has been used as a yardstick for the future. Masefield added that he believed that by 1962 the 1955 levels of air traffic would be increased by 160 per cent. In round figures that meant that at that time 6,500 aircraft of all kinds would crowd the skies with a capacity of one hundred and sixty million passengers a year and twenty-seven billion ton-miles. He added: "I believe these guesses are pessimistic."

5

As far as Douglas was concerned, the Masefield pronunciamento was three years too late. In June, 1952, a Special Project office had been established within the company. It was extremely hush-hush. The publicity department had been instructed to say that Shogran, its head, had been sent to Europe to make an inspection tour of jet-engine developments there.

The office—which mentioned the DC-8 only in whispers or sometimes in exasperated screams—resembled a hive of specialists. They had been drawn from every part of Douglas to collaborate on the first ideas of what the DC-8 should be. The dozen members of Douglas who were admitted to the secret were like worker bees huddled around the queen bee of their ideas.

It was not a matter of sudden inspiration. The need for the DC-8 and the capability to build it had been on the minds of most of the men for years. In the peculiar fashion of aviation design and engineering, which look ahead for decades, they all had their own mental sketches of what was needed. In general, there were five yardsticks that had to be met.

First: engines. Shogran and Raymond had bounced around the country in 1943 with a proposal for a jet-engined experimental plane testing out airline reaction. They were not satisfied then; they were not sure now. But the modified J57 engine (now called the JT3) of Pratt & Whitney offered a good deal of hope. They felt they could go to the engine manufacturers and demand guarantees of performance reliability and fuel economy and get them.

Second: runways. It was generally felt that with such engines the short 5,600-foot runway at Chicago could not be used by a jet transport to get to San Francisco. This was a problem because of the slow initial acceleration.

Third: geography. The runway question led immediately to alternative suggestions. The New York airport had a 9,000-foot runway. Using this, a larger plane with more fuel would be possible—possible enough to get to Los Angeles from New York. The idea of a London-New York flight followed. External extra tanks, wing-tip tanks, wings crammed with fuel were suggested. Since half of the weight of every big plane of this kind is fuel, the place to put it is a riddle that is always with the idea men.

Fourth: passenger capacity. In many respects, the size of the passengers decided not only the size but also the shape of the DC-8. Unlike other major jet transports, the passengers were considered from the beginning. It was discovered that the place where discomfort began was at the shoulders. Human beings had to have room to shrug. Room for four seats abreast was designed on the model of roughly the DC-7 capacity. Then the sentiment shifted toward the seating of five—then six. It shifted back to five and finally ended at six. This gave the needed width, and it also proved that there was a glaring necessity to redesign the whole interior to serve all six equally well with the least loss of time.

Fifth: cost. This was largely an unknown quantity that only time and the customers could decide. How much the airlines were willing to spend for such a massive creation, how many they would buy, these were all speculations in the future. "You know," mused one Douglas designer, "we'll never be able to own a DC-8. We won't be able to afford one."

The DC-8 project decided to commence with people. It worked out intensive studies on the order of a 95 percentile reckoning—leaving out the 5 per cent of people who were either too tall or too small. They designed the diameter into a bulging dome. They got the length by merely counting noses on the number they had to include to make a flight economically feasible. The average of filled seats on piston-engined flights was running about 65 per cent. The jets—at their projected cost—could break even at about 52 per cent and start to show profits.

"We realized," Shogran said, "that we had to figure on an entirely different environment for the DC-8. We were moving into a region where there were hundreds of little differences that meant everything to the success of the project. The DC-8, we felt—rightly, as it proved—had to be a trans-sonic craft, a mixture between. Some of the speed of the air over the wings and their leading edges would be supersonic, as it would around the cockpit windshield. On the other hand, no farther back than the tail surfaces, it would be subsonic."

<h2 style="text-align:center">6</h2>

The concept of the Big Eight stretched and contracted, bulged and retreated almost every week. "It was a little like having the foundations of a house moved a couple of inches every now and then while you were trying to put up the superstructure," remarked Shogran. The engines kept being improved; the dimensions kept shifting in order to insure human comfort. Nor did the customers stay with the pace. The British Overseas Airways Company was one of the interested spectators and advisers, but eventually they decided against the Eight and bought another plane. Pan American, United, and others stuck with Douglas despite the fact that it began to seem that the DC-8 would be behind its competitors in appearing on the airways.

From June, 1952, to June, 1955, the struggle to make the DC-8 what everyone wanted it to be and still make it a clean and workable and efficient airplane continued. At that time the decision was made—not a complete go-ahead, but at least a grunt. "It was up to Douglas at the end," said one of the project designers. "Nothing out of left field; it was a decision we could all feel coming. One day we told him we thought we ought to go, and he grunted."

It had been three years. Douglas had spent more than three million dollars simply in making the preliminary studies and the tentative design, the "exploratory phase" of the DC-8.

It had been a big job. One by one, the supports the company had depended on had fallen off. Customers like American; the suppliers who had made optimistic estimates. Even the military, the long-time friend of Douglas, had failed them. In 1953, Douglas had expected to get government money to help work out the problems of the DC-8. The engineers felt they could double on the big passenger ship and use it as a tanker for the Strategic Air Command.

At a cost of about $650,000, they had spent months in working out the design for a jet tanker. It was a good job, bigger than the competition, just as fast and as stable. The proposal was sent in, but before the evaluation of the various items was finished by the Air Force, some urgency in the procurement division gave an order for twenty-nine of the competition's tankers. It meant the diversion of approximately $100,000,000 that Douglas had hoped might come to its coffers.

This left the firm stranded momentarily. The blow was severe and the consequences could not be guessed. It was the grim drive of Douglas that firmed up the situation: he decided to go ahead on his own in an extraordinary maneuver.

Douglas took on the DC-8 as the first totally privately financed big-plane project in the history of the aviation industry. Not a penny from the military helped develop the Eight. It was, dollar for dollar, the largest single venture of its kind on a single product in the world.

7

Rumors commenced to spread. The airlines got complaints that the airports would have to be drastically altered to take the DC-8. There were complaints from suburban dwellers about the possibility of being dispossessed for longer runways; of being driven insane by the noise of the jets. "Monsters," the DC-8's were called in the local newspapers; in Switzerland, preachers held meetings and denounced the manufacturers as "scientists devouring man."

The hullabaloo did affect the DC-8 concept. Yet viewed in its essences, it came down to only two points: were the runways long enough, and were they thick enough to withstand the Eight's take-off run and weight? The noise was already being taken care of, as far as possible, in another division—possibly the most expensive single investigation in the history of Douglas.

Experts examined the runways and facilities of the major airports. While the examiners admitted that a few terminals might have to lengthen their runways to 9,000 or 11,000 feet, depending on altitude, these were to be in the great minority. Most of the airports discovered that the large commercial transports such as the DC-8 would take off at less than the maximum weight at less distance. Only the great nonstop terminals for overseas or cross-country routes would have to be revised for flights of 4,500 miles or more.

No one worried about the strength of the runway, taxiway, and apron of such terminals. They were deemed adequate because of the wide distribution of the weight of the jets, even at maximum gross weights. Cross-wind landings, rate of climb, and jet exhausts were thought to have negligible effects.

Nevertheless, the DC-8 began to take shape with all these objections in mind. "The public be pleased" was the thought uppermost in the schemes of the planners.

8

As if to bedevil the engineers and designers further—the dozen men who would later go out and head up the various task forces on the production line—the problems increased. The J75 thrust was increased from 14,000 pounds to about 15,800 pounds. This alone produced welcome headaches. No one wanted to throw away the extra power, the most needed item in the whole kit. But it could be traded for a number of things: shorter runways, longer range, bigger configuration. These items had to be decided.

Moreover, the sales staff started out for orders in July, 1955. They went to Europe first, where the customers had originally insisted on a "continental range" of the DC-8, not just a landing at London. Nat Paschall, the boss of the salesmen and vice-president of the company, went with Shogran and did the talking, while the project head observed and investigated in private conversations. "We couldn't make too many changes at this point," Shogran said. "It's like putting your heart from the left to right side: it displaces a lot of other organs in your body."

Paschall did not commit himself. He addressed the prospective buyers of foreign airlines with the same phrase. "We are going forward with the DC-8," he rasped. Shogran kidded him in private. "What do you mean by 'going forward'?" he asked. Paschall shook his head. "I don't know," he confessed. "We can't go into production until we get orders, and we can't get orders until we go into production."

It was a matter of wetting a finger and finding out which way the wind was blowing. To see if the customers were satisfied with the marks on the sheets of paper they showed them; to see if the price was right; and to see if the promised performance met their needs. In the end, it was the hard but intangible fact of the Douglas reputation that won the day. Long ago, in the Martin factory, the young "pencil eater" had been secretly laughed at because he did nothing but make marks on paper. "Does he think the marks will fly?" one of the workmen grinned. It was precisely those marks that gave the DC-8 the needed impetus back home in Santa Monica.

SEVEN:

DOODLES ON THE AIR

1

THE PRELIMINARY ideas of Douglas on the DC-8 went back to the drawing board in a hurry in January, 1954. The scurry was caused by the midair explosion of one of the prototypes of the first commercial jet transport. It was a BOAC Comet in flight. It appeared to have blown up without discernible cause. Another accident followed in April. A year before, in March, 1953, a Comet crashed in Karachi, Pakistan, killing eleven people. An Indian court put the blame on structural defects. It had marked the first such disaster with a commercial jet transport—less than a year after the first Comet had gone into service in May, 1952.

Douglas himself sent a cable on the crashes. It went to De Havilland, the makers, and offered sympathy and any technical or theoretical aid possible. It was a sincere gesture. Unlike many industries with competing companies, the aircraft manufacturing business feels an accident to one hurts the whole. Viciously they may compete in good times; when they suffer, they spring to each other's aid.

The same Good Samaritan attitude was apparent in January, 1960, when the famed Lockheed Electra turboprop transport

93

seemed to rip apart in the air. Robert E. Gross, head of Lockheed, told of what happened almost immediately:

"The seriousness of this kind of development and the possible implications to any company making airplanes (ours included) are some of the most sobering elements of this complex business we are in. The effects of these accidents, particularly to a new series of plane, have in some cases resulted in groundings. This is an extremely distressing experience for any aircraft company to go through.

"Our company went through a grounding of its Constellation airplane in 1946. It brings back memories of some of the most profound moments of my life. During the worst phases, Mr. Douglas found time to call me up and urge me to keep my flag flying and to keep up my courage. He felt that in the end things would work out well. He went on to say that he had a good understanding of these crises himself and they could happen to anyone. Ironically enough, the same thing happened later with his DC-6 model and he had the same deep emotional experience to endure."

Such accidents could and do happen to any airplane manufacturer. The roster of disasters in the air in a selected fifteen-year period shows that 28 out of 73 accidents happened to Douglas planes—generally considered the most airworthy. Almost none of these could be attributed to defects in the planes themselves; the number reflects only the vast number of Douglas creations flying.

Nevertheless, the Comet disasters plunged the thinkers at Douglas into a deep study. They had seen and consulted with the British in the give-and-take of airplane design. They had expressed doubts and given advice which apparently had been ignored. Douglas designers felt that the Comet did not have enough of a safety factor: "The stress levels were too high," said one. The pressure was too much for the thickness of the skin (it was found out later that the aircraft had literally exploded in the thin high air). The rivets were countersunk instead of being "dimpled." This reamed out little knife edges that induced a tendency to shear the rivet as the skin shifted. The bending-in process of Douglas kept the strength while not affecting the rivet.

"I can tell you we took a hell of a lot longer look at rivets and windows and doors and stress points," said Carlos Wood, director of advanced engineering planning for Douglas. "When you get up that high, a failure in the fuselage is as bad or worse than a failure in the wing."

2

It was a typical hesitation in the Douglas scheme of things. Research could tell the builders a lot. It could tell them more, as long as as they wanted to listen. But they had to make a decision to go ahead at some point in the future. They had commenced dreaming of the DC-8 as a full-blown airframe as long ago as 1947 —the year the DC-6's went into full service.

"It was the new power plants of the military jet engine that got us to working on the frame," said Wood. "A new design in a power plant, a departure from the old, with more power and efficiency and simplicity, always intrigues an airplane maker."

It was a case of matching advantages with penalties—tossing the penny of speculation endlessly, heads over tails, and seeing how it came down. The speculation, not all of it authorized, went on and on. It came out in memoranda, in sketches, in dreams, in talks in little bars in Santa Monica and Long Beach. "It was a period of exploratory cogitation," said Wood.

At this time the end of the piston engine, as far as aircraft were concerned, was in sight. The manufacturers had the choice of more and more cylinders, of more and more complexity, of more and more repair and maintenance. They hesitated to advance into this jungle of power where the engine might fail because of its very design. Not only that, there had clearly been an economic decision made which was out of the hands of Douglas. Less and less money was being spent on researching the piston engine. More and more was going into the exploration of jet possibilities. "The piston-engine money was settling down into something like main-

tenance and replacement," explained Wood. "The turbine idea—
not yet a pure jet—was coming into its own. We started to plan
on our own pure jet, however, to be flying, in our estimation, about
1955."

As it proved, they were about four years off. This was a normal
guesstimate. Douglas figured about eight years as its average to
produce such a revolutionary product. From 1947 to 1951 for
planning and research; then the big decision in that final year, and
four years more to build, pick off the bugs, and get the prototype
certified. "This was our average, you understand," Wood declared.
"Sometimes we've had sports that we've built in two years of work,
and some non-sports that have been built in seven."

Whatever the time element was, Douglas was depending hugely
on the jet-engine builders such as Wright and Pratt & Whitney and
Rolls-Royce. The engine was unreliable; it was hard to service and
maintain; and, above all, its fuel economy was unbelievably bad.
In some cases it consumed 50 per cent more than a piston engine,
so much that the fuel load for even a short distance made it impossible to heave off the ground. Nor was the thrust satisfactory.

"We kept watching and saw the engine boys working," Wood
went on, "and they were highly successful in their modifications.
We commenced to have a good deal more than a hope." At the
same time the virus of success attacked the high echelons at
Douglas: they were having such phenomenal luck in stretching the
DC-6 to the DC-7 to the DC-7C that they were unwilling to shut
off the bonanza. Nor did the airlines, their customers, want them to.

Moreover, the military developments were going on, and the
information about these "experimental" jet engines was funneling
back to the Douglas files. It could be used, reworked, and revised;
and each day spent in such research was bound to pay off in commercial transport.

3

In 1945, two years earlier than Douglas, such airlines as United
had commenced to take interest in the military jet and its vehicle.

Even while the airline was putting the DC-4's back into their regular post-World War II runs, a section of engineers was assigned to make a thorough study of the turbine engines both as to the propeller and pure jet. By 1947, when Douglas commenced to simmer, the interest of United was widely enough known so that another major aircraft manufacturer offered to build an eight-engined turboprop craft that could cruise at 540 miles per hour with a load of 40 passengers. Cashing in with the DC-4's, United turned down the offer as uneconomic.

Three years later, the United engineers went to England. They personally flew one of the first De Havilland Comet transports. They came back impressed enough to report that in their opinion the jet development would eventually take over all engine work on world air routes.

These statistics were duly relayed to Douglas, as they were to other plane makers. American and TWA were also vitally interested. The DC-6 had come in, and now economic studies were projected against this highly efficient plane to compare its yield with the proposed high-level, high-speed creation. To find out more about actual flying conditions, United began a series of hypothetical coast-to-coast jet "flights" known as Operation Paper Jet. By mathematical computations and graphs, using solely paper and pencil and slide rules as their wings, the airline technicians flew two such round-trip "flights" daily for more than a year. The mythical jet had a paper cruising speed of 545 miles per hour, "flew" at an altitude of 35,000 feet, and "carried" a payload of 22,500 pounds without stopping to refuel. The studies appeared to prove that such a jet transport was highly practical—if it could be built and the customers induced to board it.

Douglas was not too happy about such developments. As late as 1951, although jets appeared theoretically certain, the airlines and the manufacturers were holding back. Most of them felt that the development of such a plane was too big an undertaking for any company without either amalgamating or getting government financing. The DC-6's and now the DC-7's were rolling along. Everyone seemed fat and happy.

Moreover, there were not the refinements that were needed for long-distance air travel with the ground installations available. One "unfortunate requirement" that held Douglas up in its final decision was the insistence of the airlines upon a jet that could take off from the 5,600-foot Chicago runway and make it to San Francisco. No such craft existed.

But the urge to commence building was on its way. In Europe the Comet, with all its early defects, had already appeared. BOAC had Pan American Airways scared. They demanded a competitive airplane in order to protect their domination of the Atlantic air routes. "It began to look as if we'd have to build an intercontinental and a local jet transport at the same time," said Wood. "We'd have to have the hardest thing in aviation: a full-grown airplane right off the bat." More than that: they would have to gamble on the engine development.

As early as 1952, Douglas engineers had decided that by reason of the intense military development the pure jet would be commercially reliable before any turboprop engine. The latter was not receiving any military subsidy. The pure jet offered the advantages of greater speed, less cabin noise and vibration, and increasingly better economy.

Actually, in the interest of the safety and comfort of the passengers, Douglas wanted to get rid of the propeller. It gave a lot of power in a short time and could lift a big load off a short field, but it tended to limit itself at high speeds. At very high speeds and altitudes, it was actually a drag and a hazard. Since speed was glamorous to the customer and since the customer was to pay by the mile, the propeller appeared to be doomed. In another sphere of comfort, the jets promised to do away with the propeller pressure wave, which had beaten so long on the eardrums and nervous systems of passengers.

"The big jet transport might possibly have been built in 1952," said Raymond, "but it wouldn't have been very good, to put it mildly. Anyway, the big airlines like American didn't want it at that time; they wanted to amortize out the planes they already had."

4

It is easy to see why Douglas did not want to upset the rosy applecart of those years. In 1954, 35,000,000 passengers took to airplanes, a steadily advancing rate. At that time, 81,000,000 of the 164,000,000 scheduled passenger-miles flown every twenty-four hours all over the world by scheduled airlines were logged by Douglas models.

All other makes of aircraft combined accounted for the remaining 83,000,000 passenger-miles. How long and imposing the Douglas lead was can be seen from the fact that the 81,000,000 passenger-miles of Douglas were attributable solely to that company. The leftover 83,000,000 passenger-miles were flown daily by ten different American types, a dozen more built in England, two in Canada and three in France, one old German model, and 374 other models scattered so widely and accounting for so little of the total that they had to be classed as "miscellaneous."

It was a soft seat and a high one. It had been achieved by propeller-driven, piston-engine planes alone. It was a throne not easy to desert, and the Douglas loyalties are hard to unglue. But the inexorable pointing of the economic hand—the investments of the military—and the mounting interest of the hitherto aloof airlines, all pointed to a jet-engine future.

It was a future that bulged with tantalizing statistical lures. The company felt that six years from 1954—in 1960—the world air traffic would increase to 60,000,000,000 passenger-miles and that by 1970 it would amount to 90,000,000,000. It was a fair promise indeed, especially when mounted against a more ancient graph, that of 1946, when the traffic had amounted to a little more than one tenth that figure, 9,500,000,000 passenger-miles.

The old problems which had been quiescent during the "stretch" period of the DC-4, -6, and -7 now came alive once more: how to carry passengers swiftly, cheaply, and safely to their destination. The Douglas researchers came up with idea after idea. They had visions of tailless planes like docked poodles; of broad spear-shaped wings like manta rays in the delta configuration; they envisioned flying wings and flying freightcars. But time after time they kept returning to the oldest concepts of Douglas himself: it appeared that the DC integrity of aerodynamics would persist to the end of the airplaning age and perhaps beyond.

The "ground proximity" problem was one that resisted entrance into the jet age. It meant merely good flying characteristics while landing or taking off. The DC-4 had been called the "Fuddyduddy Four" for its emphasis on these items. This had not disturbed Douglas. The difficulty was in joining high-speed characteristics, which would eliminate drag, and low-speed characteristics, which to some extent depend on drag. "We wanted to get not only a plane that would operate dependably in service and fly as fast or faster than our competition," said Wood, "but we also wanted a big plane—and one that would operate in lousy weather, at zero ceiling." This desire, of course, brought up the opposite: the high-speed problems of keeping control, cleanness of structure, and staying away from yawing or fluttering at various altitudes and speeds.

All plane design is an aerodynamic compromise. It can be a noble one or a wretched one, depending on intuition, experience, and sound scientific principles. In the proposed DC-8 the objective was to attain maximum ground proximity safety without compromise in high speed. And the Douglas engineers had an ambition. Said one to his opposite number of another company in the competition: "I want to die happy. I want to beat you three times. We did it with the DC-3 against the 247; we did it again with the DC-4 against the Stratocruiser; and I'll bet we do it again with the DC-8." Said the other wearily: "You hideous character!"

5

The work went on. The information on military work filtered through from El Segundo and was digested. The mysterious explosive decompression of the Comet was checked out on the C-133 military-transport fuselage. More than a pound of additional pressure was worked out, above the Comet's limits, up to about eight and a half per square inch. Nobody liked the idea of a movable stabilizer with its implications, but the necessities of design made it part of the whole. With the piston engines gone, it became a puzzle as to where to put the wheels when retracted. They brought them up into a little box just behind the wings, into the fuselage.

A second look was taken at the windows with their double panes and frames. Outer panes (but never inner) had been broken on the DC-6's by the violent threshing of a broken antenna outside. It was decided to make them triple. It was also decided that the DC-8 would be so constructed that it could dive down to a livable altitude in less than a minute, and that the cabin would remain pressurized, even with a hole in it that let 350 cubic feet of air per second escape. Individual oxygen masks were added to the equipment. "People on a flight like that, who had an accident," declared Wood, "might get a severe headache, but they wouldn't die."

The designers were obsessed with the idea not of making sure but of "making damn sure." The windows and doors were reinforced on the plans with heavy forged frames. The use of the highly expensive but very strong and light titanium was recommended. The goal of flying endurance was put at a minimum of 30,000 hours in the air for the DC-8. It was expected that it would go for more than 45,000 hours—or a life in the air on the average of somewhere between ten and fifteen years.

The pilot's cockpit was re-examined. Since there is about two and a half inches between a man's eyes, supporting posts of less than two inches in width were planned on so that no object outside could be hidden by the strut. No metal except steel could adequately support the weight of the two-inch-plus windshield panels. Despite its weight, steel was agreed on. There had been complaints in the early transport and some in the later military models that there was "fogging up" when taking off or descending. This was rectified by having a continually heated pane of plastic included. There was also the possibility that the window might be cracked or "crazed" or otherwise covered so that the pilot could not see. A side window was devised, which, by tricky engineering in the wind tunnels, could not only be opened easily at the highest speeds but could also be peeked out of without mussing the hair of the pilot.

Extra windows were installed at spots where hundreds of experiments proved that the pilot had a blind spot. All the "must-do" equipment was placed so that one man could operate it—and with five men in the cockpit, all qualified to fly, it was assumed this was a high-enough safety factor. One of the complaints of the pilots—in their "damned vocal way," as one designer put it—was a very homey one. Their feet got cold. In a cockpit where the masses of electronic equipment put out constant heat, where the direct rays of the sun strike in, and where a superb air-conditioning system works all the time, this may seem strange. But it was a general complaint. So the engineers scheduled radiant heating panels for the floor.

After attending to the comfort of the crew, the concentrated effort of the idea task force was turned to the passengers. According to the Old Man, "The chief problem in the development of the DC-8 was the suppression of noise." He had taken notice of the complaints from airport dwellers about the whining and booming of the military jets and their "dirty take-offs," which arose from the water injection to get maximum thrust characteristics. Once the tentative decision to go had been made in 1955, sixty acoustical engineers, aerodynamicists, and power-plant engineers dug vigorously into the problem. They designed, constructed, and investigated nearly a thousand models. They tested more than five hundred of the sound-reducing devices at 10 per cent scale.

At 20 per cent scale, 350 variations were tested—and a final selection of 38 types at full scale. The most effective, based on a simple design by the Rolls-Royce Company of England, was a nozzle at the rear of the jet engine. It had a suppressing cross section that resembled a daisy with eight petals. It reduced the sound level by ten decibels—actually comparable to that of the DC-7 piston-engine exhausts—while reducing the thrust by only 1 per cent.

At this point someone took fright. "What about the dangers of that red-hot exhaust blast from the jet engines frying someone as they pass?" he demanded. No one had an answer until they tried it themselves. They found that by the time it passed the tail of any theoretical DC-8 it was cool enough to be harmless. Nevertheless, "clamshells" reversers that cut off this blast and acted as brakes (giving 40 per cent anti-thrust on landing) were invented.

6

In 1956, an economics-minded engineer of Douglas, Richard Shevell, offered factual proof that the decision of the company to go ahead with the DC-8 had not been in error from a commercial viewpoint. Everywhere he looked he saw brilliant prospects for revenue.

He pointed out that a DC-8 such as was being created, flying at a range of around 1,000 miles, had a 22 per cent lower operating cost than the DC-6, previously considered the most economical airplane ever built for its size and capabilities. According to Shevell, "Where the passenger traffic will justify an airplane the size of the DC-8, a large jet transport can be economically operated over almost any existing airline route." Contrary to early thinking, Shevell added, "A jet transport does not have to dash up to about 40,000 feet, but it may be scheduled at any altitude between 20,000 and 40,000 feet, according to the dictates of wind, weather, and the requirements of traffic control."

Competition became a worry at this stage. The early default of the Comet had injured the faith of the airlines, but the British were making great strides. The Russians were the real question marks. "They knew that planes depend upon good engines," said Wood, "and they had been developing really good military jets. Whether they would adapt to commercial use, we didn't know. As it happens, they haven't come into world competition—not as yet, anyway. When they do, with lower wages and technical excellence, we'll start to shiver." As for the competition in rocket motors, the Russians may have an unbeatable edge if they choose to begin that particular race of power and design.

"The only real obstacles," sighed Wood, "consist of the perversity of animate and inanimate objects." The cramped business of getting the monstrous landing gear tucked away so that it would not create drag had caused a controversy about breaking the structure and line of the wing. It had been decided against. Now the same argument arose about the engines themselves. European design, in many instances, had included the engines in the wing structure. Douglas decided the other way. Mounting the engines in pods beneath had both advantages and disadvantages. It allowed for more fuel within the wing, but it meant a low mounting that would possibly scoop up damaging debris from the runway. A low landing might ruin an engine, but the separation of the two allowed a major safety measure against failure or fire. The "off-loading" of the aerodynamic lift required less structure and less weight and allowed basic alterations. Finally, the engines would be more accessible for maintenance and repair.

The final design of the engine pod was set so that the whole $190,000 engine would snap off under extreme stress or emergency, in order to prevent the ripping-off of an entire wing. In a test flight in May, 1959, a hard landing made into a cross wind tore free the plane's left outboard engine. It damaged the engine next to it, crashing into the fuselage near the tail. The skin buckled but did not suffer serious damage. The test DC-8 landed under its own power and taxied safely into its hangar.

The landing gear itself was the subject of considerable revision.

It was felt that the wheels in line no longer did the job as they had on the DC-7. What was needed was a better turning radius and less "scrubbing" of the wheels. It was decided that eight wheels (to match the increasing weight) mounted in two carriages of four each would be the answer. They were arranged on a castering swivel, which locked and unlocked automatically at various angles to insure maneuverability of the big plane. This, with the safety factors against blowout and overheating, represented a minor triumph but one of the proudest. "Do you know," asked Raymond mildly, "that we spent more money on developing the landing gear of the DC-8 than Douglas spent on developing the whole DC-3?"

Even the size and shape of the windows came in for intensive examination. Forty-two different types were studied, and the one finally picked—with the beguilement of the passengers in mind—was the largest possible, about 15 by 18 inches. It was decided to attempt to make the chairs recline as low as possible.

7

Flying at the altitude of 35,000 feet is flying in a different world. Anyone up there has the strong feeling that he is approaching the limits of his own cosmos and verging onto another. The aircraft is flying over most of the atmosphere, although it is still in and of it. Most of the clouds—excluding a few massive thunderheads that extend to above 40,000 feet—are below the plane. The "gusts" and "holes in the air" are less than 10 per cent of those experienced 15,000 feet lower. The vision is much clearer and comprehensive. On a clear day, from 40,000 feet, the view will cover a radius of 246 miles—an area that may include several states or a great deal of ocean—compared to the radius of 174 miles from 20,000 feet.

In order to support the 150 tons of weight which the DC-8 would eventually represent, the wing research was most important of all. It was one of the last major items to jell in the minds of the designers. It was agreed tentatively that it would be a swept-back design of a unique camber pattern, but just what the final version would be, no one could tell.

By 1956, the trickle of orders had begun to flood in. Some sort of picture of the future of large commercial jet transportation could be seen. The estimate was that in 1958 a dozen such transports would be delivered, none of them American. In 1959, it was prognosticated, 92 of them would be flying—of which 57 would be 707's and 22 would be DC-8's and the remainder of foreign manufacture. In 1960, it appeared that 122 would be scheduled to be delivered—32 to be 707's and 87 to be DC-8's and the rest foreign. The backlog of indicated orders did not go further. It may be added that these expectations have proved to be considerably below the fact.

It was estimated that one DC-8, flying over the Atlantic, would carry 60,000 passengers a year—almost as many as the total of the passengers on the annual trips of the $70,000,000 U.S.S. *United States,* the world's top steamship.

Research descended close to the ridiculous. One project measured the resistance of the pilot's pants to the seat. Five different types of wool gabardine were solemnly rubbed across the proposed seat in the cockpit with "a motion somewhat resembling that of a person sliding across a seat." The rate of rubbing was sixty-eight a minute. The fact that this might indicate an extremely fidgety pilot did not seem to bother the researchers. They came up with the relieved conclusion that no appreciable shine was produced in the gabardine. All Douglas pilots got recommendations to wear the stuff.

EIGHT:

THE CLEAN SHEET OF PAPER

1

"*WHENEVER* we're stuck," said Raymond, "you know what we do? We sweep everything off the desk and lay down a nice, clean, fresh sheet of white paper."

In 1956, the report of the Douglas Aircraft Company to its stockholders wrote off about $18,500,000 for the development of the DC-8. In 1957, it was announced that approximately eight thousand Douglas employees were constantly employed in research and development—in every field from high-energy chemical fuels, aerodynamic lift, nuclear-propulsion systems, sound suppression, miniaturization, to electronics—to the tune of $57,000,000.

Of these extraordinary amounts, it is fair to charge the DC-8 with a large proportion. It is the last plane of the air, the only one of its sort—too, it is the seething practical test tube of the future. Its place in aeronautical history will be determined not only by what it does but by what it prophesies.

Although the Eight must be considered as a whole plane, it may also be divided into the final design of its parts. The ultimate judgment is how such a creation flies and lasts; but the first tentative opinions are put down on the clean sheet of paper and crystallized in the first model produced. After that any craft—and the DC-8 is included—may be modified almost beyond recognition. Its essentials must remain the same if it is to have the same fundamental performance.

In making as final as possible the design of the first batch of DC-8's, the engineers in charge realized they labored under a time disadvantage. Boeing had been doing more work with jets, although Douglas had pioneered the field. Boeing had had the orders for the jet tankers. Boeing had the prototype of its 707 already flying. Douglas had only its personally financed concept.

Doomed to be second in the race against time, Douglas determined to be first in quality. Although the first commercial jet transport to fly successfully would have a great edge, it was not necessarily decisive. The later transport would be able to embody all the developments coming along so rapidly in the many interrelated fields of aeronautics. True, a competitor could revise and make over, but this would be a fantastically expensive second thought of manufacture.

Contingent upon the demands of the airlines—which had suddenly seen the light of jet capability and felt the heat of customer demand—Douglas would keep its final design as loose as possible until the last moment. (How loose this was became obvious a couple of years later: the first and "final" specifications of the DC-8 length were 139 feet, 9 inches in 1955; by 1960, they were 150 feet, 6 inches. The wing span grew nearly two feet in the same period.)

The sales force was already out, hawking the wares of a product not fully determined on. No one could foresee that by November of 1956—a little more than a year after orders were solicited—the company could announce for the first time in its history that 50 per cent of its business was purely commercial, out of a total backlog at that time of $2,200,000,000.

2

In the fall of 1956, Raymond made an acute analysis of the properties necessary for a successful commercial jet transport. He admitted that speed was "fashionable," but he cited other over-looked values. Economy: "By equal dollar values, the fare has been reduced from 5.9 cents to 2.6 cents per mile." Comfort: "Com-posed of many elements: low noise level, air conditioning, mini-mum cabin altitude, space to move around, lack of vibration and bumpiness." Travel facility: "The ability to schedule a trip to any section of our country, to any country in the free world, and count on air carriers to get there." Reliability: "Today we conventionally make appointments that depend on the schedule by air being main-tained."

He pointed out that the upcoming DC-8 had been tested in 1954 against a study of the proposed DC-7D, a turboprop version, and that the figures had proved that the cost of operating a pure jet was almost as low, equally far in range, and 150 miles an hour faster. Comparing the DC-8 against the "most economical airplane in the world," the DC-6B, he found that the new design would effect a cost reduction in nonstop Atlantic flights of 22 per cent.

Most important of all, he pointed out that MATS—with much more experience in airlifting passengers and freight than any com-mercial line—had declared that "air transportation depends upon an integrated air-transportation *system* composed of aircraft, per-sonnel, airfields, weather forecasting, communications, navigation facilities, ground handling, air traffic-control facilities, logistic sup-port, maintenance standards and procedure, rules and regulations, and, above all, good judgment. The whole system must develop and grow with the aircraft. The potentiality of an aircraft out of phase with the rest of the system is never fully realized."

Raymond added his own pair of additional requirements, "which are peculiarly important to the commercial air world," noise sup-pression and "the question of business sanity." It was a textbook for the fining-off of the problems of the DC-8. If the huge plane could not be landed on existing facilities; if it could not be easily handled on the ground or in air traffic; if it could not be easily maintained; and if it was not quickly responsive to the judgment of its pilots—then the DC-8 would in the long run be a failure.

It was part of the whole. Its function was to stitch together all the components into a massive workable unit. This was all the more important because Raymond could not foresee a "surplus of important aircraft" since the machines were never built on speculation but on contract to meet the traffic demands of the airlines. They, in turn, were faced with ascending curves of passenger requirements.

3

The man who buys single pieces of equipment for his business at increments of more than $5,500,000 is likely to be finicky about the purchase. He is not likely to be pleased with the general run of assembly-line models. Each DC-8, the designers knew, would have to be made on a mass-produced economy basis. It would have to have in addition hand-tooled, custom-made variations. Good a selling point as this might be, it also became a knotty expense. The first fifty DC-8's—both domestic and intercontinental —found that three different power plants and nine different customer configurations were required.

The time element, though largely played down, was also an item in the consideration of the final design. Douglas decided, in order to clip months off the production schedule, to go ahead full speed into production. This meant dispensing with building a prototype and waiting for the results of the tests on the ground and in the air. The research had been thorough. The conclusions were based on a long history of know-how. Douglas decided to use the familiar technique of manufacturing a production airplane immediately. The first nine of such planes off the assembly line would be used in a mass test-flight program. This amounted to roughly the same idea as that of automobile makers in Detroit. It had proved feasible for them to take stock cars off the assembly belt and put them into tryout racing programs.

Douglas experts felt that a virtually handmade prototype must naturally have differences in performance from a run-of-the-mill plane. Even if the former were passed by the test crews, it would prove little about the assembly-line product. It would be better to prove the worth of the actual product that would go to the airlines rather than the worth of its model.

After the prime consideration of the available power of the jet engines had been solved—three models became available, the Rolls-Royce Conway, the Pratt & Whitney J57 and J75—the next most pressing item was the design of the wing. It was the subject of long and heated arguments. The significant parts of the design of the DC-8 are generally related to the configuration of the wing and the outside and inside of the fuselage. (In the engines, the power is essentially the same as that for any jet airliner.)

There exist only two known ways for a big plane to attain speeds just under 760 miles per hour, the highest speed of sound. The DC-8, with its four jet engines, can attain nine tenths of this speed without too much effort and perhaps even momentarily cross the sound barrier on the back of more thrust. Taking the plane along with the engines is another problem.

This problem involves reducing drag. This may be done by making the wing sections very thin and strong. This forces the fuel back into the fuselage, to the potential danger of the passengers or cargo. In a military plane, where the pilot considers himself and is considered by others expendable, this is not a consideration. In the X-3 and other models, Douglas had discovered that a thin wing could break speed records, but it pushed the fuel inboard until it became a factor that disturbed them. "We have never mixed fuel and passengers," said one designer, "and I don't think we should start now."

The only other solution pertinent to the problem was the swept-back wing, a device long known to aeronautical investigators. While the thin wing cut through resistance, the swept back allowed it to slip by—although not without some sacrifices in lift and stability. The DC-8 engineers realized that in order to be economically competitive with other pure-jet transports of the future, they would have to consider this conventional wing design already used by a major competitor. It included a 35-degree sweep back.

What Douglas aeronautical minds did not like about this specific angle was that it rendered the plane somewhat unmanageable at low speed and in landing.

What resulted from the discussions was a unique Douglas design, in accordance with the traditional insistence of the company on safety factors. It was decided to make a stronger wing, swept back only 30 degrees. It was discovered that such a design could still remain competitive while giving added factors of strength, maneuverability, and safety. Such a design sprang directly from extensive air-flow analyses and an expensive wind-tunnel program. The total spent for DC-8 wind-tunnel tests alone ran to nearly $10,000,000.

This broad design was modified slightly in some ways to unearth the most ideal compromise between speed and safety. Although it borrows from many sources, it is thought by Douglas to be special in its field. One of these modifications was the creation of reverse-camber inboard and an increase in the camber of the outboard sections of the wing.

One unusual result may be mentioned. Comparing the performance of the DC-8 to that of the propeller-driven DC-7 series, the normal cruising speed of the Eight became 57 per cent greater, while its final approach speed—where slowness is desired—was only 14 per cent greater than that of the DC-7.

4

This naturally brought up the enigma of how to construct such a different Douglas wing. The problem of wing strength and its joining to the fuselage—customarily the weak point—has always been a foremost Douglas concern. It is here that most of the stress may be expected to appear on any craft.

The ideas advanced included the splicing of the wings at the intersection; continuing the wing itself into the fuselage for a center splice; or "forming" the intersection of the wing into the skin of the plane.

The last design, the most expensive and difficult, offered the best ratio of weight and strength. Combined with the center splice, it proved to have top efficiency in obtaining long life for the whole installation. This combination was what Douglas finally adopted.

With this went the traditional three-spar construction of the company. The idea of only one or two spars was discussed—one spar rightly made could support the whole—and it ended by three spars being used. Despite the added weight, it was felt that the added safety was highly desirable. It meant that any single spar could fail under extreme conditions. The other two would bear the weight without difficulty and with a respectable margin of fail-safe factor. The wing itself was a surprise to the profession. Using reverse, or upside-down, camber in the inboard section, the whole structure looked topsy-turvy. It proved to have unusual lift and strength and handling characteristics.

The swept-wing design also had to be corrected in another way. The wing is poorly adapted for control in the danger of cross-wind landings at airports. The Douglas engineers countered this by incorporating larger rudder deflections and a higher tail. Even so, the maximum allowable cross-wind landing for a DC-8, the most stable of the swept wings, is only 30 miles per hour. The Eight can land even when it has to crab sideways along the runway as much as six degrees off the center line.

Still another improvement to increase speed was the use of cambered pylons on the engine pods suspended from the wings. The normal straight pylon mountings had accounted for more than 20 per cent of the total drag on the airplane. With the cambered type, no drag of this kind seemed to appear until the speed of the Eight hit somewhere above 600 miles per hour.

Installation of the engines was based on accident and crash data from airline, government, military, and engine-manufacturing sources. Douglas did relatively little research on this except to design the plane and its weight so that the failure of a single engine would have almost no effect upon the Eight itself. To further eliminate any contagious engine failures, it arranged the operation of each engine to be independent of any other.

Powerful aerodynamic high-lift devices, such as leading-edge slots and flaps, were installed on the DC-8 to give additional boost at the take-off. Conversely, to give drag in landing, the most modern "spoilers" were installed to kill speed and lift.

On the tail design, the Douglas design came full flower. The tail of the Eight has been designed to be useful at speeds hundreds of miles beyond the capability of the wing without losing control at any time. This construction came about after some of the famous Douglas studies in this region—the tail being a trade-mark of the plane. They proved that the tail and its construction become more critical than wing design at next to the speed of sound.

5

The delay of Douglas in building allowed the company to lay down some unique features on the Eight. These included new landing gear, fueling and servicing techniques, and the protection of the engines against runway debris. The design had already departed from the competition in its less abrupt sweep back of the wings and the fuller configuration of the cabin in order to make the passengers more comfortable. Now Douglas added touches that were selling points.

By using larger landing gear, with the four-wheel bogies, it was discovered that the complete castering of this made it possible for the Eight to make a 180-degree turn on a 91-foot circle as compared to an 88-foot circle for a DC-7. Pressure fueling required only 20 minutes; servicing of the needs of the passengers, including food and water, took only 30 minutes. Efficiency studies determined that the passengers could leave by the two big exit doors within six minutes. Or, if they preferred to use the emergency chutes, within three minutes.

The final problem was one of preventing any one of the four powerful engines from sucking up loose articles on the runway.

This had always been a problem for the military until Douglas solved it. The invention was an aerodynamic "screen"—a device called a "blowaway jet." This was no more than a diversion of part of the huge amounts of air sucked into the jet-engine opening, so that any suctional vortex was appreciably destroyed without the efficiency of the motor being impaired.

6

Possibly the feat of which Douglas was most proud in the original Eights—and certainly one of the great problems of the jets themselves—was that of the suppression of noise. The elementary point was that noise meant power. If all noise were suppressed, no engine would have a pound of thrust. It seemed an inevitable evil necessary to the success of power. Douglas refused to believe it. The company started out to work on the idea that noise could be kept down to acceptable levels and that eventually it could be broken down to the point where even the sensitive ears of airport residents—who have been one of the chief complaining agencies—would be satisfied to some extent. It was largely because of the objections of these local residents (near the plant) that Douglas has spent up to $30,000,000 on noise suppression up to 1960, with studies still continuing.

What has happened is encouraging. The noise levels have now been brought down in the jets to the levels given off by the old piston-engine transports. In some cases, they are actually three decibels lower. Douglas does not believe they can be materially reduced below this point unless there is a technological breakthrough that divorces noise from power in the engines themselves.

The final design of the Douglas "noise suppressor" grew out of 4,500 separate test runs. The steel-petaled daisy fastened behind each engine, in essence, merely a very elaborate tail pipe—on the order of an automobile muffler—dissipates the exhaust energy of the jet engine very rapidly. Douglas made a further use of this discovery by using the suppressors as "reversers." The braking effect of the device was a clear corollary to the noise suppression. "We tried to make the DC-8 acceptable to the public on the ground," said one of the designers, "and we got an extra safety feature."

Fire aloft has always been a major consideration of the Douglas planners. The DC-8 was finally equipped with seven kinds of fire protection. These consist of fuel dumping, sealing-off, segregation of hazards, fire walls, fireproofing, extinguishers, and mechanical devices.

The fuel may be dumped through the vents, a total load being disposed of in as little as six minutes. The various internal air spaces may be totally sealed off from any outside air supply and the fire thus smothered. All potential or actual hot surfaces are carefully segregated from the fuel tanks. Fire walls were planted at the upper and lower end of each engine pylon, as well as a fire wall and a secondary sealing-off partition in the wings. Materials in or near the "hot zones" are fireproof, and metals such as magnesium which burn with great intensity that approaches explosion are used minimally despite their relatively low cost, strength, and lightness.

One of the increasing dangers of fire aboard the jets—a peculiar problem in flying, made more acute by modern engines—is the static-electricity discharge. Such charges are built up by the friction between the fuel and the carrying line and may be brought about as well by the same causes in the hydraulic systems. Since jet engines use a higher flow rate of fuel—as well as a heavier fuel— than piston engines, the danger is increased. Douglas met this by a simple but ingenious invention—a gimmick that has the rising fuel itself close a possible spark gap in the feed before the charge becomes dangerous.

Birds pull their feet within their feathers when flying to reduce the drag of flight. On the DC-8 the drag of the extended landing gear alone is about one and a half times greater than that of the complete airplane with the gear retracted. This gear is operated by two separate hydraulic mechanisms. If both fail, the gear may be lowered by hand. The number of wheels on the landing gear is scientifically related to the load put on each wheel and the airport pavement, just as a truck uses a certain number to support its load on the highway. The DC-6 and DC-7 had four main wheels to support a load up to 143,000 pounds. The DC-8 was to use eight main wheels, plus the two nose wheels, to support a load of 310,000 pounds.

The tires on the landing gear—which cost about $250—are good for roughly 75 landings. The brakes must be replaced at a cost of $750 every 400 landings. This high rate of deterioration is understandable when it is known that to support a DC-8 in landing it takes 450 times the amount of effort that it takes to support a car stopping at 70 miles an hour.

7

Possibly the roughest requirement of the design of the DC-8, one that had never happened to the company before, was that it was an entirely new plane. Previously the engineers had been able to take over components of previous planes (even in the DC-4) or modify them in such a way as to make them acceptable for the construction of the next model in the series. The design of the DC-8 called for discarding all previous parts; new tooling was demanded almost from the most minute rivets to the skin of the cabin and wings.

Design problems multiplied seemingly of their own accord. The ventilation system was not perfect: every seat was tried in turn and one—and only one—had a draft right at the back of the neck. The engineers redesigned the duct and found it worked, but it had added seventy pounds to the total weight of the plane. Each DC-8 finally got an air-conditioning system that cooled enough air for fourteen homes.

Plans were made for the assembly line. An estimated thirty-nine weeks for the construction of each plane was figured on for fabrication and assembly—making a forty-six model gap between the finished product and the first parts coming onto the line. This was speedy, considering the six million separate items that have to be mounted with the delicacy of the hairspring of a watch—some of them as big and tough as girders, others not much bigger than a pin. A sample of the early care taken lies in an assembly-line sign: *Do Not Carry Drinking Cups Beyond This Point*. The reason: if a paper cup fell inside the frame unnoticed, it might cause a suspicious rattle that would cost literally thousands of dollars to locate and correct.

While the plans for the DC-8, which would eventually cost $6,000,000 a copy, were going ahead, a sure indication of its popularity was moving at its own sedate pace. A toy company was miniaturizing the blueprints to make a twelve-inch model out of plastic in fifty-four pieces—at a tooling-up cost of $50,000. Naturally, it had to be approved by Douglas.

One Douglas feature that is little known but invaluable was the "external store." It consisted of a hook-on device whereby an airline could fly a spare engine to a crippled sister in an outpost such as Guam—an engine that might boost its original $150,000 cost by a couple of thousand dollars if it were carried any other way.

The design called for nearly 14,000 pounds of cargo and baggage to be carried in pressurized compartments fore and aft. There was even an animal compartment in the forward cargo space provided with all the comforts of home for the "transportation of four large dogs."

The doors were intricately designed so they would not fly open under pressure from the inside. There are authenticated records of accidents where other high-altitude planes popped a crew member into the air over the ocean like a squeezed watermelon seed. The Douglas doors lock themselves in such a manner that inside pressure itself helps seal them. These same doors were tested for efficiency in evacuations: three thousand people of every age, weight, and size handy went out to make sure of the efficiency and speed of any exit made in emergency.

8

The design of the DC-8 was appreciated abroad as well as at home. Chief Engineer J. T. Dyment of the Trans-Canada Airlines, in a paper read to the Canadian airline pilots, spoke of the "concept of doubling the speed, doubling the operating altitude, doubling the weight, and doubling the number of passengers that can be carried—all in a single step—" as fabulous. He said dryly, in mentioning the landing speed of 151 miles per hour, that "we are grateful that this is not also double."

He estimated that a big jet transport of the DC-8 caliber would do four times the work of a piston-engine transport, but that it would cost about $1,000 an hour to operate and that the grounding of such a craft would make the penalty of lost revenue four times greater. He described the cockpit arrangement for the benefit of the pilots, telling of its new devices.

The DC-8 flight compartment was designed for a basic two-man crew with the layout such that either pilot could operate wholly from either seat. Electrical- and fuel-system controls—set prior to flight and needing little attention and no adjustment during the time in air—were on an aft panel. Nearly all the other controls and indicators were on panels mounted in the front so that both men could see and use them. Improved vision came from a low, simple glare shield, and "eyebrow" windows added to the vision. An integrated flight system computed together some components: it gave accurate indications of air speed, angle of attack, Mach number, altitude, true air speed, outside air temperature, and ram air temperature. The altimeter especially had been made accurate to about a quarter of 1 per cent—100 feet in 40,000 feet altitude. "Take-off monitors" told the pilots whether ground acceleration was enough to lift off and whether there was time enough to decelerate. Automatic flight recorders took down plane and engine data. Such tapes could be processed by electronic computers and gave a complete, accurate summary of the plane and engine performances, or could be radioed to the home field for appraisal there by experts even during an emergency.

Two systems of oxygen—one for crew, one for passengers— operated automatically. If the cabin decompressed dangerously in a tight spot, the door of each passenger mask compartment would pop open. The crew had its masks ready at all times.

To insure radio reception, Douglas engineers designed a series of antennas. An overwater DC-8 may have as many as twenty-five of them. Lightning protection—and statistics indicated that the DC-6 and DC-7 airplanes suffered an average of one and a half strikes of lightning per year—would be provided by small metal-foil pieces on the radar dome which would dissipate the bolt and cause the current to flow harmlessly along the outer skin and off into space.

In the whole of its design, Douglas demonstrated its reluctance to abandon safety for the flashier facets of speed and aeronautical fads. The emphasis was not only on getting the passengers—and the four large dogs that might travel in the luggage compartment with fresh air at 60 degrees—to their destination but on getting them there comfortably and whole.

"As far as we know," said one of the Douglas designing group, "there is no passing fashion in human lives. If we don't get the occupants of a DC-8 to where they want to go, alive and in the style to which they were accustomed on the ground—if they vanish in midair owing to some defect we overlooked—it may not be murder, but it has echoes of manslaughter."

Curiously enough, these ideas did not hurt the popular idea of speed. That differential between competitors over which some of the airlines had worried never showed up. The DC-8 had been downgraded by some of the aviation rumors as slower than the 707. A report from a United engineer covering six-week periods across the country for all major transcontinental airlines (during the last of 1959) showed little difference between the two. On

California–New York flights, the average margin between the two was about two minutes—one way or the other, depending on the winds. Other surveys by various airlines proved that by 1960 the DC-8 was the fastest jet transport of its type (in eighteen separate models) in the world.

NINE :

THE FLIES IN THE TUBE

1

A HUGE TUBE of aluminum alloy, twelve feet in diameter and one tenth of an inch thick, blasting through a black-blue sky eight miles up, at a speed of ten miles a minute. An interior filled with strong bright rays of unfiltered sunlight and blinding reflections from cloud layers and haze below. The air outside, a cool −60° Fahrenheit, amid a roaring gale of from 500 to 1,000 miles an hour.

More than 140 people, two hundred times a day, pay cash to put themselves in this kind of situation for periods ranging from three to twelve hours. Nor is the faith of today's generation misplaced, depending as it does on the skill of such aeronautical designers as those of the Douglas company. Living in such an environment, without the ameliorations of science, could be the counterpart of Dante's ninth ring of hell. As it is, the predicament is more comfortable than a placid evening in 95 per cent of the living rooms of the United States.

A passenger may stroll the length of such a tube, from one cocktail lounge to another, with a brimming glass in his hand. Nor will he spill a drop unless his own unsteady condition causes it. He may read a small library of magazines and converse with a variety of fellow passengers without raising his voice—unless in his own anger. He may fall asleep to the muted lullaby of high-fidelity music. European investigation of this musical psychology has disclosed that modern piano music is appropriate for take-off, such compositions as *Rhapsody in Blue* are excellent for landing, and that any work of Johann Strauss is good for cruising.

His surroundings are those that royalty in their best days could not afford: specially loomed fabrics, tenderly engineered seats, flattering illumination, solicitous attentions. Food comes hot from the griddle to his own personal table, freshly made in a flying kitchen. He may retire to a lavatory where the conveniences are more modern than and as efficient as those in his own home.

Possibly the only things he cannot do are take a bath and step outside to stretch.

The sum total of the interior of a DC-8, as far as the passenger is concerned, is much more than home ever was. It is, if statistics may be believed, much safer. It represents one of the latter-day triumphs of interior engineering.

2

Outside the industry, not many people care about the exterior of the DC-8. What they are concerned with is the inside, the elaborate room where they will be carried to their destination. From the earliest days of aviation passenger-carrying, this has been an aim of the manufacturers.

In the thirties, the big, battleship-like F-32 Fokker transport—with its curious twin-engine mounts that displayed motors back to back—had tapestried panels, luxurious couches, flambeau lighting, scenic windows, elegant drapes. The Boeing Air Transport Company added trained nurses as the first airline "hostesses." The mammoth Swiss DO-X that flew a demonstration tour over four continents for the German Lufthansa line in 1930-31 was sumptuous. So much so that, when it took off from New York, its twelve engines had too much weight. For eight long hours the plane never rose more than 50 feet from the waters of the Atlantic.

The interior designs of thirty years ago were necessarily hit-and-miss. Planes were so new, the environment of the air so unique, that little could be done. What has slowly evolved in the history of aeronautical interior design is the viewing of the problem as part of the making of the whole plane.

An industrial designer who approaches the enigma of the inside of such a plane as the DC-8 is faced immediately with severe limitations. These are invariably matched with extreme demands. The shape of the passenger pouch is usually that of a cylinder with a no man's land of cockpit at one end and a toilet at the other. The designer must deal directly with the inexorable necessity for the utmost in aerodynamic cleanness, structural integrity, and economical lightness. Within these limits, he may work freely; beyond them, he has no choice at all.

He must create the illusion of much more space than he has. In some instances, he must make it seem larger; in others, he must have it appear cozy. Partitions, color and texture changes, mirrors, even "musical screens," are used toward this end. Different forms and optical illusions created by artistic patterns are used to attack the most difficult problem of all: to increase cabin width.

Claustrophobia, the dread of closed spaces, is a growing problem with travelers. It must be fought with all the genius and trickery at the command of design. In order to insure that he gets his fair share of real space, the airplane interior designer is on hand at every design change. He must make sure that he has enough headroom, hip room, shoulder room, leg room, and mental room for the passengers. He must argue violently for more floor area and window space. He must demand adequate maneuvering room in the lavatories, galleys, coatrooms, baggage racks, and for other human needs that might arise.

Nor can the designer rest on his laurels when he has achieved these demands. He must realize that any great passenger aircraft is not a volume-production item. Only a few hundred will be made, in most cases, as in that of the DC-8. The final result must suit a multitude rather than one man: such a plane, with its proved long life, may eventually serve as many as fifty different owners in the course of its usefulness.

This makes it mandatory that the interior be styled once basically for the original maker-customer. It must allow at the same time for variations to suit the taste and pocketbook of other airlines. To achieve the maximum in effects, the designer works closely with the manufacturer and the first purchasing airline. Some airlines have their own consultants. They submit ideas to manufacturers such as Douglas, who will modify and adapt them to the hard necessities of flight.

Attention is paid to the interior of the DC-8 chiefly in one direction: the comfort of the passenger. This is secondary only to the needs for the plane to fly safely, speedily, over long distances, for a reasonable price. "We're like kids who have caught flies in a tube," said one designer. "It's up to us to keep them alive and happy and to let them go at their destination in a mood that will bring them back to fly again. The DC-8 must be their second home, a home in the air."

"When you pay five and a half million for just one tool of business," said an airline operator, "you want to be sure it fits your transportation needs for a long time—unless you take up flying rajahs exclusively." The heart of the demand is for flexibility. The DC-8 is capable of having what is called a "super-deluxe-blue-ribbon" interior with sleeper berths and a couple of cocktail lounges with from 100 to 120 passengers on the elite Paris–New York run. Within two or three hours after landing, about the same time as it used to take to dress up the interior of a DC-3, the DC-8 is ready to take off for South America with 140 to 150 hard-bitten tourist passengers—the seats being six abreast instead of four and the berths being replaced by bag racks. In actual practice, the whole interior of the DC-8 is designed to be redone at least twenty-three profitable and different ways, on a literal inch-by-inch basis.

3

Lighting the interior is a special challenge in the DC-8, as it is in any plane that flies for passenger comfort at its altitudes. At 40,000 or 50,000 feet, above the highest clouds, the light of the sun is intense, full of unfiltered rays. The rate of cosmic rays slashing through the shell of alloy is greatly increased. None of the rays increase to the point where the length of passenger exposure forms any kind of hazard to health; what is created is a topsy-turvy world of light.

The light from the sky is not as intense as it is on earth. The light from below, bounced back from the fleece of the clouds or the land-and-water of earth, creates a brilliant reflection in the cabin. This is psychologically disturbing to some. The old decorating rule is that the dark colors belong on the floor and the lighter ones on the ceiling, in accordance with nature. In the case of the DC-8, this is met to some degree by simply reversing the color schemes: the dark floor colors on the ceiling, the lighter ones on the floor. This causes a slight reaction of wooziness in some cases. It becomes genuinely different and enjoyable after a short exposure. A companion problem, which was solely the worry of the airlines flying DC-8's, was the bleaching power of the sun at high altitudes. This has not been solved. Usually the seat upholstery must be replaced in less than a year or two: the color is gone by that time.

Lighting within the DC-8 also plays an important part in the "life" of the passengers aloft. It is adjusted according to the weather: to compensate perhaps for the mood of the group; to alleviate nervousness or to induce sleepiness. A complete spectrum of special lighting is available to the crew. Aiding in this color "mood psychology" is the music that is specially selected to strengthen the whole.

A Douglas failure in an area where Douglas likes to do as much as possible of its own research and construction was the building of lighting fixtures. After spending $50,000 on trying to design its own ineffective lights, the company turned to an organization that specialized in devising lights for Pullman railroad cars and Greyhound buses. Out of this collaboration came a special lightweight fixture that was both easy to clean and to replace. It gave control and direction to the light, which concentrated a beam on the passenger's lap without disturbing a neighbor.

4

In 1932, the situation of a passenger on a plane was pitiful. Bucking storms on almost every trip, making a dozen stops to load up with gas, shooting up and dropping down, rocking from side to side, without food or drink except at the hasty stops. It was an ordeal through which the bravest could not pass unscathed, which often made even the hardened pilots vomit.

Worst of all, perhaps, was the noise and vibration. Some of the early pilots, like Howard Hughes, found themselves more than a little deaf from the constant beating of sound and shaking on the eardrum. For more comfort, the passenger could use free wads of cotton to stuff in his ears—and converse with anyone in the square cabins by lip reading.

As long as piston engines drove propellers, such vibration and noise were almost inescapable. It was not until the DC-8 and similar jet passenger carriers that both the noise and the vibration vanished—not completely, but enough to make an astonishing difference in the mental and physical attitude of the men aboard. Instead of the earplugs—which would have weighed about a half pound for 150 people—Douglas chose to stuff more than two tons of scientific soundproofing material into the walls of the main plane cabin. It was a costly decision. It meant that the weight in passenger payload would be reduced so much that a fleet of twenty such jet airliners would lose the equivalent revenue of about $50,000 a day. "But we wanted them back to pay for the return tickets," explained Douglas laconically.

There were some visible returns in cash. Although the DC-8 has achieved the best yet in food service, it has actually saved money over such flights as the DC-4. Each of its two galleys is capable of serving seventy top meals out of a kitchen no bigger than a couple of phone booths. Each has the weight of no more than an empty filing cabinet. But the stewardesses simply do not have time to get around to all the passengers. On inter-city hops—such as that from New York to Chicago—there is no time for a meal since the trip takes only an hour and a half. It was found to be impossible to serve a passenger on the average of one every thirty seconds. The effort was given up.

What was substituted was fresh coffee. A grinder that whips up the coffee beans into a brew as fast as it can be poured is now standard equipment. So are special liquor-mixing attachments that do allow the hurrying hostesses to get around between take-off and landing. If the planes get any larger and the flights any faster, the hostesses will have to use devices like those in the huge Douglas plant itself: roller skates or bicycles.

5

There is a sea creature of colorful exterior called the anemone, the flower of the sea. Although it has none of the structural integrity of the airplane, it has one characteristic in common. It is one both repulsive and useful: under stress, it regurgitates its entire inner lining and within a few days grows a new set of innards.

There is no better miniature of the subconscious desire of the interior designer of an airplane. In the demands on him to make a potential inferno not only healthy and habitable but also happy, he feels an incipient stretch that borders on schizophrenia. He is not being asked to design for an earthly domicile or a heavenly one; he must settle for something in between. Nor can he make use of the habits in which he has been trained.

The shape of his interiors is always dictated by aerodynamic requirements. He cannot exceed them. He must yield to a rigid framework whose very being has been dictated by structural integrity and economic lightness. His job thus becomes one with sharply defined limits. He sees clearly how sharp they are when he is first brought in as a consultant in the initial design stages. He remains on guard constantly. "The engineer always forgets that there are human beings involved," complained one designer. "It's our job to remind them of it."

The interior designer must also have the courage to demand that the passengers be allowed, as far as possible, to discharge a normal way of life as they would on the ground. He must fight for enough room for lavatories, galleys, coatrooms, and even space for baggage and emergency gear.

This meant that interiors should be built only to be revised in half a dozen ways. Lounges should be convertible to seats. Movable bulkheads should be able to separate various classes of passenger traffic. Movable seats should contain all passenger utilities. On those planes that carry sleeping berths, these should be designed to be quickly converted to bag racks. Even coatrooms should have facilities to be transformed into a lavatory, and shaving stations make a cocktail bar.

As far as plane-interior materials are concerned, it became wholly a question of weight, safety, cost, wearability—and the individual opinion of the purchaser. New fabrics and structural materials are constantly being designed that in color, lightness, durability, and convenience are infinitely superior to anything previously available. A point all airlines like to make is that they like to be sure their DC-8 is still in stylish service three to ten years after they have bought it.

Developments on the way include individual listening devices which will enable each passenger to hear his favorite radio program without disturbing a neighbor. Television shows will become a standard item. If television entertainment is not available, the screen may reflect a closed-circuit movie of the country beneath, even though it may be covered with clouds at the time.

6

The discovery that passengers in the DC-8 spent less than 4 per cent of their travel time out of their chairs led the Douglas engineering designers to concentrate a major part of their efforts on this segment of the interior. What they developed might be called a personalized chair. It is reminiscent of the mechanically gimmicked couch that used to be popular with the bedrooms of the Hollywood rich. Almost every conceivable item that might be needed is built into the chair. Reading light, call button, cold-air control, emergency oxygen mask, even a folding tray with its individual light, are integral parts of it. This is in addition to obvious conveniences such as magazine pockets and ash trays. The chair itself is mounted on a floor track which may be adjusted to the required space. Feeder lines for the chair utilities are plugged into the side wall.

The seat cushions are molded layer-foam construction specially developed by Douglas. They have been designed to fit 90 per cent of the traveling public, from a diminutive Japanese to a skyscraping Swede. The chairs have been tested for exact degrees of firmness, angle of back recline, position of armrests, and length of leg stretch. The padding itself is contoured to suit the normal position of a seated passenger. The seat belt is strong enough to hold a load equal to twelve times the weight of the heaviest person.

The development of these "Palomar" seats cost about $250,000. Production cost ranged from $200 to $800 apiece, depending upon the degree of luxury required by the customer airlines.

7

The surface of the earth is seven-tenths water. The atmosphere, under normal conditions, contains about 13 per cent water. In a DC-8, eight miles or more in the air, water is not only scarce, it is a substance that could make up the single biggest leak of profits.

Every pound of water carried means a pound less of human payload. Since water weighs 8.67 pounds per gallon, the enormous weight factor involved can be visualized, if the needs of each person are taken into account. Nor is this all: the passengers not only need water during the trip as fluid intake, they also bring aboard with them an amount of water in their bodies that will have to be disposed of before the trip's end.

Water is a necessary nuisance in air transport. United carries about 80 gallons of fresh water for 120 passengers. Pan American, however, carries about 120 gallons for 135 persons—slightly more per capita because of the longer nonstop flights on their routes. Flushing water for the toilets is separate; it amounts to about 55 gallons each.

Water "habits" account for some losses of it aloft. If a woman wants hot water for washing, for example, she usually wants it at a specific temperature. If it does not seem warm enough, she lets it run until it achieves the desired temperature. Airlines and even airplanes as big as the DC-8 will never have enough fluid for this kind of person. Aircraft water-supply tanks used to be kept electrically heated to 100 degrees by immersion heaters. The water is now heated by a small flash heater under the sink which gives instantaneous hot water. Hot and cold come from the same faucet, simply by dialing the desired temperature.

The water in the air of a big plane's interior is a baffler in itself. With up to 150 passengers breathing in the confined atmosphere, as much as 15 pounds of water an hour may be given off. This would ordinarily condense in a sort of miniature rainfall were it not for the device that takes care of such a constant emergency. The interior air is constantly mixed with incoming air and is discharged outside.

8

"The most important development in commercial flying in the last few years?" repeated Shogran thoughtfully. He grinned. "It's not the jet engine or the swept-back wing. But it's something that might make its inventor as famous as the Wright brothers." He sat back. "The flying flush toilet," he said.

The DC-8 is an airliner that carries a secret weapon for promotion. It is a complete sanitation system, symbol of the devious research, the peculiar questing of Douglas. Under law, no flying vehicle may discharge waste overboard. In order to meet this requirement and still provide for the comfort of its passengers, Douglas developed a 300-gallon septic tank in the belly of the DC-8. Two to six special flush toilets, similar to those used in any home, were installed. They used reclaimed waste water from the washbasins as the flushing agent.

These same toilets, however, brought up a problem that none of the engineers had thought of. As might have been expected, it was concerned with women. It appeared that the feminine contingent on the proposed DC-8's felt that the flush toilet should be able to carry away literally any object they chose to throw into it. Since Douglas could not alter the feminine psychology pattern, the problem was finally solved by using an enlarged version of the familiar garbage-disposal unit. This ground up the debris in the toilet bowl and allowed it to descend to the flying cistern below.

Air conditioning within the cabin was a riddle with which Douglas was very familiar. The prime objective of the engineers was to do away with any recirculation of used air. The scientists knew they had to create a pleasant temperature for the majority of passengers, regardless of outside conditions. There also had to be a sufficient flow of air in both cabin and cockpit to remove odors and smoke and provide good circulation without creating a draft. All this had to be done in spite of the fact that the individual cold-air jets for each passenger were continually changing the temperature levels.

The final solution consisted of bringing in fresh air from outside. It was instantly pressurized and heated (or cooled) and pumped into the cabin at a rate that gave complete air change every three minutes. An unusual feat of temperature control was the achievement of holding the cabin at 70 degrees Fahrenheit when outside temperatures dropped below −100 degrees.

Even in these days when everyone pretends to a smattering of science, the pressurizing of the DC-8 cabins is not altogether understood. Many passengers still believe they are exposed to the old ear-popping. There is a favorite pilot story of the old lady who asked a pilot not to fly above five thousand feet because the altitude hurt her ears. Rather than explain that the cabin was kept to limits well within her endurance, the pilot—on the run to Mexico City—explained: "Madam, your ticket is for Mexico City. That is already seven thousand feet up."

"Is that so?" cried the old lady in alarm. "Then I'll stay home. I thought it was on the ground."

TEN:

THE DARING DUNKERS

1

IN SPITE OF the infinite care and trouble lavished on any aeronautical creation, there will always be accidents. The law of gravity itself, which man temporarily "violates" every time he flies, is not wholly responsible. Errors of the human senses, the malfunctions of mechanical gadgets, are more often the cause. But of all the elements that take part in flight, possibly the safest is the structure of a plane like the DC-8.

Before it rises into the air, its performance can be largely guaranteed. This is possible because of the extensive preflight testing that is endured by the structure on the ground. This in turn is realized by the extensive use of the mock-up.

Such a word is relatively new to the general public. Fifteen years ago it was unknown except to a select minority. It can be generally taken to designate a replica of the object under test—either full scale or less—that is supposed to instruct or inform the investigators about the real thing.

Mock-ups can be divided into various classifications. A "specimen" may be a sectional mock-up; a "model" may be a scaled-down replica. But their function is generally the same—to ferret out the defects that might later show up in flight. Before a commercial plane is built, between the design and the prototype, another step must intervene. To bring about successfully performance and safety, design is not enough. There must be an imitation plane that is a plane in every detail, except that it is molded in wood and plaster and will never take the air. This scarecrow of aviation is the interval on the line between concept and testing production. Here the mistakes may be ironed out cheaply and finally.

2

Mock-ups of the DC-8 took several forms. The first metal specimens were constructed in 1953 for testing fact against the theory of stresses and fatigues. Later another section was built exactly as the cabin and part of the fuselage of the DC-8 would appear. It was used in water "atmosphere" testing. The third and best-known, a massive wood-and-plaster affair with the configuration of the DC-8 as it is today, was shown to prospective customers in the summer of 1955. It is significant that the first considerable order from Pan American for twenty-one of that model came in October, only a few months later.

The first general molding of the DC-8 was on paper. This was the paperwork, which might have been called a mock-up of sorts. The design continued through more than 28,000 drawings—the smallest about eight by eleven inches and the biggest three by sixty-five feet. By weight alone, these papers ultimately equaled the weight of the airliner itself.

The next model of the DC-8 was a miniature clay one which presented the general aspects of the Eight as it might expect to be. After this, a small steel model was built to microscopic exactness for wind-tunnel tests. It was placed into the mechanical blast for months, and the results were studied again and again. Here the first equivalents of how the DC-8 might be expected to perform appeared. Because of the confining of the air and because such models cannot be quite exact, the results were not perfect. But these were the figures on which the aerodynamicists had to depend until the first test flight would correct and approve them.

Then came the real mock-up, the full-sized wooden cabin and cockpit. It was built inside a huge hangar and much later hauled outside for the plant visitors to view. Its purpose was to present the interior designers and engineers with actual spatial relationships. The arrangement of ducts, wires, pumps, compressors, tanks, and similar items had to be haggled over one by one and fixed in their spots. Invisible passengers had to be placed in the most comfortable relationship in a full-sized setting.

This version was surprisingly realistic, even down to the final red-white-and-blue paint job which was put on the first genuine model. The exactly scaled DC-8 mock-up cost Douglas more than $7,500,000 to build. It was an inch-by-inch replica of the real thing except for the tail. Woodcarvers even placed little representations of the instruments in the cockpit. (Each Eight contains more than a ton of wood, from carved panels to lavatory doors.)

As an "airplane" that would never fly, the mock-up cost more than $2,000,000 above what a flying production model would later be priced to the airlines. It served a special purpose. Arranged as the ultimate DC-8, surrounded by a picket fence on the runway with stairs built fore and aft, it was a visiting point for hundreds of engineers and airframe designers. Studying their project life-size, they had an opportunity to examine future points of discussion at first hand. The mock-up was credited with eliminating hundreds of "bugs" in the blueprints themselves. It provided nearly as many production short cuts for use on the assembly line. "It proved to be worth almost exactly twice what it cost us," said one Douglas executive. "I mean by that, in time and effort and material saved."

As a sample of the intricacy that the nose section alone of the DC-8 mock-up had to express, the later construction took 1,500 separate parts, not counting rivets and screws. Aluminum, stainless steel, and titanium were riveted, welded, bolted, or screwed together. It was a prime aid in the building of patterns and jigs that were needed for 4,500 major parts of the plane. And as the engineers made their calculations outside; inside, the interior-design stylists tried out their colors and comforts.

3

If the fuselage of the DC-8 is thought of as the designers planned it to be built, it divides naturally into three sections: the nose, the cabin, and the tail. The wooden imitation comprised only the nose and cabin, as did the mock-up for the underwater testing. It was nearly 124 feet long, with a height of more than 20 feet. Only certain key components were built of metal. A full wing was attached on one side; the landing gear extended and retracted and all control surfaces operated. On the inside, the most minute details of the hydraulic and electrical systems were mounted and studied and revised. The air ducts and the location of all items that might contribute to passenger comfort and safety were tested in relationship to the future plane of metal.

One preliminary sectional mock-up was built to contain five seats abreast. It was changed to four abreast. This was agreed upon, and the mock-up was sawed up and given away for children's playhouses and dog kennels. Then the design was changed; another mock-up was built, and the seating arrangement went back to five abreast and made flexible enough to take six.

The final mock-up design proved some very vital points. When the seating arrangement rose to five and six abreast, it was obvious not all the passengers could reach the upper racks. Nor could they obtain the same service. Douglas immediately eliminated the traditional overhang—even taking out screwheads—and put the facilities into their super-secret seat. They thus got not only more convenience for their passengers, they also produced the feeling of more room, as in a super-railway car. It vastly improved the "clean" appearance of the lines and boosted the psychological optimism and "free feeling" of the passengers.

In 1954, United built a full-scale cabin mock-up of "a generalized jet transport" at San Francisco. Exhaustive studies were made of the best location for seats, buffets, lavatories, and other installations. These summaries were passed on to Douglas (and others) to aid in the final cabin design.

In the United version, experimental seatings were made to get maximum comfort either for first-class or coach service or a combination of the two. There were dozens of meal-service rehearsals to test the effectiveness of the buffet design and to determine how many stewardesses were needed for various kinds of flights.

In the middle of 1955, United assigned a technical and management team to work full time on all aspects of commercial jet-transport operations, maintenance, and service—in essence, a mock-up committee.

4

The DC-8 was at length modeled basically on the work that had been done on the DC-6 and -7 fuselages. The greatest secret of the whole was the arrangement of the interior. "It was kept more secret than most military work," said Wood. At several points, "spies" from rival manufacturers were detected trying to sneak in and sketch the interior. Cameras were strictly forbidden to anyone.

While the jiggering of this sample was going on, other parts of the DC-8 were being "mocked up" one by one. The idea was to get the whole tested only after each of the parts had proved its individual worth.

A cross section of the fuselage was stuffed into a huge icebox-*cum*-furnace, where it was subjected to temperatures from 60 degrees below to 150 degrees above zero. Hundreds of electronic thermometers were planted in the section, as a doctor might thrust the same thing into the mouth of a patient. They gave much-needed hints about air leaks, drafts, and the reactions of metal and glass. In a concrete vault, other technical observers watched through shatter-proof glass windows while various structural parts of the DC-8 were manipulated into tortured forms. Parts of the fuselage were pre-tested to over 12 pounds per square inch, although other tests indicated that the materials themselves could take over 40 pounds per square inch. This was equated against the normal DC-8 cabin pressure at cruising heights of no more than 8.7 pounds per square inch. It provided a sea-level atmosphere at an altitude of 23,000 feet. At 40,000 feet, the "cabin altitude" was 6,700 feet. (This can be compared with the old pressure of 4.1 pounds per square inch in the DC-6 cabin, which provided a sea-level atmosphere up to 9,000 feet.) The triple-paned windows were tested on the specimen mock-up sections up to eight times the normal pressure. They demonstrated that the multiple construction prevented virtually all fogging up.

One of the old DC-3 defects in the cockpit used to be the inadequacy of the waterproofing around the windshield. With a DC-8, going through the air at a speed just under that of sound, raindrops were likely to strike with considerable force. Even much lower speeds used to squeeze a good deal of wet through edges of the DC-3. In the early days, many a pilot had to bring along a raincoat as standard equipment. It used to be a joke on the DC-3's that there was "light rain outside, heavy precipitation inside." The engineered pressurization sealed this off in the DC-8 despite its considerably greater momentum and maximum visibility.

5

On the other problems, the Douglas engineers called in airline advisers, pilots, and government safety experts. Midair collisions were a prime concern. The assembled experts did not believe that even if the pilots were seated in a totally transparent bubble, it would provide a guarantee of avoiding other craft. They knew that the pilots of at least three jet fighters, in similar cockpits, were involved in clear-weather collisions with large commercial transports at lower speeds.

The fact of the matter seemed to be that, at modern rates of acceleration and cruise, the principle of "see and be seen" in the sky was not a foolproof means of avoiding collisions. At jet speeds the rate of closure had become so fast that it was possible that the sharpest-eyed pilot could be deceived. Even if a speck in the air (not on the glass) was seen, the seconds necessary to identify it as another airplane, to determine its course, and to take necessary evasive maneuvers ate up enough time to make escape unlikely.

Nevertheless, it was obvious that the Eight had to have top visibility plus all possible automatic warning systems.

The DC-8 cockpit ended up with 21 square feet of glass area. The glass was 2½ inches thick, held in some places by one-inch steel posts. This arrangement allowed the pilot, without moving his head, to see 20 degrees above and 15 degrees below a horizontal eyeline. A slight tilt of the head would increase the vertical angle of vision to nearly 80 degrees. By turning 70 degrees to the left, the pilot's vision was expanded to 90 degrees upward and 29 degrees down. The left-to-right vision from the pilot's seat totaled 233 degrees—127 to the left and 106 to the right. Since the copilot had the same visibility in the opposite direction, the total angle of visibility-seeability came to 254 degrees out of 360 possible.

In developing the cockpit mock-up, the testing engineers suspended two small metal spheres from the ceiling to represent the eyes of the pilot and copilot. Using this as the center reference point, the most important controls and instruments were located so that they could be seen or reached without movement or with minimum movement of the head and eyes.

Any cockpit windshield needs to be remarkably strong to resist not only different pressures at different heights but also to resist the importunities of birds. Government regulations provide that the always-present hazard of a goose, duck, or even an eagle challenging an airliner shall be summarily met. The "bird-impact" tests require that the glass shall resist the impact of a four-pound duck hitting the windshield at cruising speed. To attain this, a compressed-air blast blew a dead four-pound chicken through a pipe and against the glass at a rate of about 460 miles per hour. The Douglas inches-thick surface was proved to be 23 per cent above requirements.

The last of the major cockpit problems was keeping the glass clear in rain or snow or hail. At 35,000 feet such phenomena as two-inch-thick hailstones may be expected, and ice forms very rapidly. One C-133 had been riddled with "stones from the sky" in the form of hail and had not suffered too much loss of maneuverability or safety. But it was decided to design the DC-8 to operate safely under continuous maximum icing conditions. The long wing and shorter tail surfaces, as well as the engine pylons, came in for special design of a lightweight cyclical hot-air system. It used the heat from the engines to clear away any frozen crusts. As a "wiper," the same hot-air blast was used to clear the windshield during snow-, ice-, or rain-storms.

6

As one of the most important specimen mock-up tests of all, Douglas created a great water tank in a Santa Monica building. Here, since the plane could not be tested in the air as yet, it was subjected to the "atmosphere" of water, which could duplicate all the stresses and strains of the upper air while still remaining under scientific control and observation.

A 50-foot section of the fuselage and cabin was immersed in the specially built tank. The section contained every critical DC-8 structural detail. Over a period of months it was deliberately subjected to all the situations a commercial transport plane might encounter in service, including the embarking and disembarking of passengers.

This forward section survived the fatigue of over 140,000 take-offs, flights, and landings. This is the equivalent of 120 years of flying service by the DC-8. Each "flight was deliberately severe, using the water to duplicate air turbulence to a point far beyond that so far reported in actual flying." Every "landing" was a bounce landing, highly abusive to all the gear.

This was done in the span of six months. The tank was fitted with hydraulic devices intended to work under water. These were designed to produce structural fatigue damage in every sense that any engineer's imagination or previous reports had detailed. Cabin pressures, inertia forces at landing and take-off, external aero-dynamic pressures and suctions, landing-gear loads, and even the loading and unloading and shifting of passengers were simulated.

In order to get realistic support behind the spars of the attached half-wing, the fuselage was cantilevered from a mock-up center-body section. Both the inside and outside of the fuselage were filled with water so that special effects of the water "atmosphere" could be nullified.

The average under-water flight (or cycle) consisted of: (1) pressurizing the cabin beyond its maximum design strength, far beyond the aerodynamic suction encountered in flight; (2) flying a "gust load" of twice the pull of gravity and reinforcing it with additional loads to simulate external aerodynamic forces; (3) violently de-pressurizing the fuselage; (4) applying a landing load in the form of a "crash" so hard that it occurs only once in an average of 50,000 landings.

The results of the under-water testings were constantly checked by a team of skin divers. These were technicians and engineers who had made this a hobby in off-hours and were qualified to detect any faults. The team inspected at specified intervals. After 53,000 cycles had kneaded the plane under water, cycles that meant a complete flight from take-off to landing, they found nothing. (It was shown that when cracks were finally developed at the open-ings, they were in the outer aluminum skin alone. That immensely strong metal, titanium, used for reinforcements along the fuselage, never yielded in any manner. The rip-stopper titanium hoops— inserted into the fuselage to stop any sudden skin tears that stress might produce—proved their worth. Not even a crack developed in them.)

It took more than 113,000 cycles to create a small crack in the machine-aluminum window-supporting plates. The tests continued —with the fuselage unrepaired—to nearly 120,000 cycles without any other appreciable developments of danger to the plane or passengers. The tests were called off simply because the engineers could not create any further damage.

What this meant was that in the under-water tests the DC-8 had endured the equivalent of one hundred years of flight. The very low damage rate proved there would be "no rapid deterioration of structure even in very old airplanes," the report stated. The actual safety in flight was reported to have a "safety level far in excess of anything demonstrated in the test." This was determined because during the fuselage tortures there was no maintenance, and "in service the airplane will naturally be maintained and repaired should a crack develop."

Further tests were performed in the water tank to find out what would happen if the fuselage skin were penetrated by a foreign object while under full pressure. The skin-diving engineers fired a fifteen-inch triangular spearhead, from a gas-loaded gun, six times into the aluminum skin. Two shots passed through the skin. Two pierced the skin and the reinforcement. The fifth penetrated the skin between the windows. The sixth was made at the intersection of the skin and a rip stopper. The report stated, "It had not been possible to produce significant crack growth beyond the ends of the spear penetration except in the lightest skin gauge of aluminum." In all respects the cracks were stopped by the rip-stopper.

The only fatigue cracks in these "120 years of service" that were developed were near the forward service door and near a window. Both these designs were improved and made safe in final production. The tests also substantiated the long-time Douglas investigations into better ways of fastening the skin to the frame by both rivets and hucks, especially in the supersonic cockpit area.

7

In the midst of these specimen tests, the forward section of the DC-8 first commenced to have its "face." From the front, seeing the smooth lines and the gaping air inlets, it appeared like an amiable, bulbous-nosed character with a toothless grin. Viewed from another angle, the inlets seemed to appear like a pair of slanted oriental eyes—an appearance that Douglas approved as likely to appeal to the Japanese airline executives.

The extent of testing on the ground was a long-seated conviction of the Old Man. As early as 1916, he was one of the co-authors of a treatise (with Hunsaker) on *The Dynamical Stability of Aeroplanes.* There is no way of telling which of the authors contributed the phrase, but it was stated that "it is likely that the most satisfactory airplane will be only slightly stable and that this airplane will be, in any possible attitude, easily controlled by the pilot." It is hard not to hear the echo of the conservative twenty-four-year-old engineer even at this point in his career. The article added that "experimental flying is dangerous," and went on to say wryly that "the designer will be very economical in his suggestions under such conditions."

Aside from the technical research done on the simulated DC-8, the general exhibition of the mock-up caused a tremendous amount of interest in the plane. This culminated even before the plane itself flew. The staff at Long Beach—where the plane was being built— struggled valiantly with a flood tide of visitors including crowned heads, board chairmen, newspapermen, and the certified curious. Mutters were heard that the facility was "the Douglas answer to Disneyland." One customer's stunt consisted of an eye-popping exhibit for a film to be used in European sales. A well-known European ballet dancer agreed to perform a special improvised interpretation of man's yearning to fly—in connection with the DC-8. Most of the film had to be made in the factory, with the massive craft as background, as the dancer alternately languished and leaped.

Not everyone had been forewarned. There was a rash of anguished phone calls from the labor force. One foreman roared into the telephone: "There's some bastard running around over here in red tights and a blue satin cape! He's *dancing* all over the place and around our plane!" He evidently thought he had a unique kind of labor problem.

The buildup was sufficient in other ways. The first orders, in the shape of letters of intent to buy, came drifting in by July, 1955. One sector of the uneasy Douglas feelings about the possibility of selling the DC-8 was being firmed up.

Reassuring signs came from other directions. In September, 1955, the design had jelled as much as was needed. It was still flexible—various components could be and were changed—but the basics were approved and irrevocable. On October 11, the order for "engineering release" was given.

This meant that the work on the refining of the design and the sophisticating of the engines would go on simultaneously with the making of jigs, molds, and parts. The DC-8 was being built from the ground up to the air, and the first of the beginning of the assembly line could get under way.

ELEVEN:

"HOW MUCH? WHAT!"

1

NOT ALL companies—not even the greatest—would have felt equipped to undertake an enterprise of the financial status of the DC-8. Douglas felt it had the background, the talent, and the cash to pull it off.

As it turned out in hindsight, even their biggest estimates fell short of what it took to carry them over the top or even break even financially in the next few years. This was not so much a result of their own figures as it was a complex of pressures which happened to meet at a certain point: inflation, competition, the building and testing of a new type of plane, and the industry itself. And it appeared increasingly sure that the massive early write-offs of costs—plus the superlative performance of the DC-8 itself—would make the years ahead the most profitable of all for Douglas.

The financial history of that company, like that of the other aircraft manufacturers, can only be described as an off-agin, on-agin, gone-agin procedure. In 1932, the DC-2 "Flying Hotel" sold 138 copies at a price of $87,000. Up to the end of 1941, the $110,000 DC-3 sold 431 models. But a pre-DC-4 model, worked on intensively for three years, had to be sold in 1939 at a loss of $1,780,000—like the 150,000-pound B-19, which cost Douglas

$4,039,000, and was sold as a single model to the Air Force for a loss of $2,644,000.

Then World War II boomed Douglas in the manufacture of military craft—some not of Douglas design—to the extent that in 1942 the company sold only 17 commercial craft, 3 in 1943, and none at all in 1944 and 1945. Until 1941, its total sales had led the commercial-transport market with 72,000,000 as against a $345,000,000 total sales. Between 1942 and 1945, the company sold nearly $3,300,000,000 worth of planes and earned a profit of less than 1 per cent.

During the next four years—1946 through 1949—Douglas sold only 281 commercial planes. Only 46 were peddled in 1948, and, in 1949, a grand total of 5. Thereafter the totals began to rise until, in 1953, 75 had been sold for a total of nearly $90,000,000—the best year for Douglas since 1947 and the $67,000,000 gross brought in by the DC-6. For the next few years the record was impressive until the new jet age forced the change-over into the DC-8.

Nevertheless, for those with long-time faith in Douglas and his judgment—and it has been his own personal and precise risk taking that has made the difference—any $1,000 investor in 1928 would have been worth about $33,000 in 1954.

Millions can drain away very quickly in the business of aircraft manufacturing. Experiment, research, unforeseeable mistakes, trying and testing take their toll; and the customer's whimsies often do the rest. Unhappily, anyone in the industry has only two customers: the military and the airlines. The military can provide 80 to 90 per cent of aerospace business, but profits are small. The airlines, in a broad sense, want much the same stylized thing, only done differently. The result is often financial chaos, especially if it is remembered that Douglas has to keep its weather research eye out on such infinitely removed projects as space stations (on which it has been working since 1946).

The year of 1960 seemed to slump in the pattern of 1945. Then, war had ceased to be a business, only to be built up again in haste in 1950, when the Korean action came along. Now, flying in the air had begun to taper off. The forward look was to missiles and the space age.

It had been foreseen. Both Douglas and Boeing had been cutting their labor force by thousands. Salary slashes had been tried. The military spending that had been around $8,000,000,000 in 1959 had been cut down to $6,000,000,000. In 1955, the profits of the whole industry—largely set by Douglas—had verged on 4 per cent. By 1960, they were only a little more than 1½ per cent. It was a situation that could be blamed on bad government co-ordination of new and old programs for aircraft and space vehicles, as well as the fact that there were more companies and fewer contracts. In all of this financial huggermugger, the old-time giant Douglas suffered with its fellows in the business.

2

In the spring of 1958, Douglas himself had called the decision to make the DC-8 "a billion-dollar expression of faith in the economic future of the nation and the world." Put into more prosaic terms by one of his lower-echelon executives, it could be translated into realistic language: "Our hand had been forced. We had to go into the building of the DC-8 as a jet transport or else give up building airplanes."

The truth was that Douglas had lagged because it did not like to be pushed; because the airlines had first dragged their feet about the jet engines and then had suddenly demanded them; and because Douglas did not have a large enough military backlog for development. As late as 1959, only three airlines operated 75 pure jets. In 1960, 92 Boeing 707's and DC-8's were in the air. During the same year, 148 more pure jets were due to be delivered to American airlines and 120 additional to foreign customers. Moreover, the passenger capacity on the huge, fast transports had been filled from no less than 75 per cent to over 90 per cent—as against a previous long-time average of 65 per cent.

In the spring of 1958, Douglas had even then spent more than $200,000,000 in payrolls and engineering, facilities, tooling, and material for the Eight. As an offset, the airlines had given him orders for approximately $675,000,000 worth of the craft. It was to prove out, by the early part of 1960, that Douglas had not yet broken even on its heroic investment.

In the spring of 1960, Douglas was in unhappy financial shape. It had been in the red for a year, and dividends seemed like a faraway dream. The president and board chairman, son and father, offered to take a 25 per cent cut in their salaries of about $100,000 and $150,000 each. This sacrifice was accompanied by a suggestion —subsequently withdrawn—that all salaried employees also take a 10 per cent cut. Although Douglas reported orders for 153 DC-8's on hand, it had been forced to raise their prices twice, a total of 15 per cent. The top tag was now a sizable $6,200,000. And the C-133B military cargo-plane program was due to stop in 1961.

The Douglas missile future showed sales promise, with Douglas selected by NASA to develop and build the second stage of Saturn and with the winning of a major Navy contract to develop the Missileer air-launched missile weapon system. The remarkable Thor program was going on, and Thor missiles had been the foundation of virtually every space exploration in the previous years. But the fate of the anti-missile missiles was up in the air. With some new A4D attack bombers scheduled and a new air-launched missile, the Skybolt, coming up with a possible $500,-000,000 order, new business could offset the $34,000,000 loss reported at the end of 1959.

The future seemed to lie within the fourteen-year-old space-program investigation of Douglas. The shadow of the DC-8 lay over this as a prototype, either for far space or for supersonic transport. Cash reserves of $35,000,000 and a working capital of $154,000,000 were available to swing Douglas over the hump into new fields, as was the traditional reluctance of the government to allow any aircraft company to go out of business.

3

One of the assets that enabled Douglas to get the cash to back the chips it had pushed out was its reputation. In a 1921 advertisement, Douglas solemnly declared that "the users of airplanes, whether they be purchasers of rides, private owners, transportation companies, or government departments, demand and get the utmost in performance consistent with sturdy and conservative construction." It went on to say that "without these basic characteristics, aircraft cannot be satisfactory from the point of performance nor as a sound financial investment. Those who know most of the importance of superfine quality and workmanship find the cost of quality a small item when measured in terms of satisfactory performance." The advertisement ended with the one statement: "Quality is the basic feature of all successful aircraft."

The basic formula of Douglas could be represented almost by a symbolic equation: $\frac{QQC.}{HR}$ Quality, quantity, and cost over human relations. Since the company sells an airplane, it must put out a reliable product or go broke. Douglas prefers to call its over-all inspection of an airplane during all phases of its manufacture "quality control."

The importance of mechanically controlled methods and scientific approach to reliability factors, however, is not wholly dependent on the detection of flaws in manufacturing. At a recent conference on quality control in which these methods were stressed, a plaintive questioner broke up the conference by asking, "Whatever happened to the man with the flashlight and the mirror?" He was referring to the earliest type of airplane inspector—the man who would check out the odd corners of a plane by illuminating them with the flashlight to see what was reflected in the mirror.

An example of the massive errors that can happen in the best-regulated corporations was met painfully by Douglas not long before the DC-8 at the cost of some hundreds of thousands of dollars. Producing 440-volt AC-powered USAF mobile training devices, the company had accepted and approved its own units. It had the first of them on the shipping dock ready for final Air Force inspection.

The Air Force inspector destroyed their smugness after the most casual inspection of one of the units. "All these," he said, "will be useless to the Air Force." The Douglas inspector denounced him. When the air had cleared, the inspector quietly pointed out that all Air Force facilities used 220-volt AC power. He was right. All the units had to be recalled, redesigned, and reconstructed.

A further instance was the installation of a compass-indicating system in one of the Douglas transports. It worked perfectly on the ground and in test procedures. However, when it got into the air, the readings were so erratic that the system was worse than useless for the long flights required. The trouble worried the inspection crew for weeks. One of them finally took the compass apart and checked it bit by bit. He not only found magnetic screws in the compass area—using a 39-cent magnet—but he pointed out that the drawings demanded them.

A third example was the installation of two bunks on the flight deck of a Douglas transport for the use of relief crews. Douglas was used to installing such bunks and did this as a routine matter. One of the inspectors took a nap in the upper bunk on company time and fell out. He inspected the brackets holding the bunk in place and reported indignantly that the first rough air that expanded the structure of the plane would drop the top crewman into the unsuspecting midsection of the man below.

Attention was called to these mistakes to demonstrate Douglas' careful correction policies. Once they had been committed, rectified, and procedures set up to make sure they would not happen again, they could be used as horrible demonstrations to the employees. Three thousand copies of this particular bulletin were broadcast to the inspectors as samples of what must not happen again. One of the warning posters in the plant showed the famous Leaning Tower of Pisa with the legend below: "Somebody Goofed!"

4

From 1932 to 1959, a twenty-seven-year period, the DC series including military versions had numbered 13,190 planes. They had not been without faults, but they had been honest craft. They had done what they were built to do—and in most cases much more. Even the fourteen DC-5's that were built in 1939 to race along at 195 miles per hour had been good airplanes, though uneconomical.

These designs had come out of knowledge and experience. Now an entirely fresh concept had to be tailored for the public and backed with money outside the firm. Although it had the breeding and background, the DC-8 could not be totally "evolved." It had to rise like a phoenix or not at all. In order to provide itself with ammunition for the raising of money on the design, Douglas conducted what amounted to a popularity poll. With intense seriousness, Douglas tried to find out what the public—rather than the engineers—wanted.

Its files bulged with advance information. All ideas crossed the executive desks, and the good ones were noted down. "The DC-8 flew right out of a suggestion box," claimed one engineer. All the notions, no matter how haphazard or wild-eyed, were deliberately kneaded into the mass of scientific knowledge and experience that Douglas had culled over the years—the mass of what-will and what-will-not work. Some of it was invaluable.

Three researchers of United, one of the great airlines, spent months in 1952 investigating the upper air where the DC-8 would fly. John Sorenson worked on upper air winds; Mel Balzer did the job on temperature; and Boynton Beckwith was assigned radar operations. They found out some new facts about the hazards the DC-8 passengers would have to face.

Some of the old difficulties turned to advantages in the conclusions of the studies presented to the American Meteorological Society. Flying at 35,000 feet or above, the DC-8 would miss most of the cloud cover and thunderstorms—although the big ones would still tower up to above 40,000 feet. The well-known "jet streams"—winds blowing in a belt 200 to 300 miles wide and about 30,000 feet deep (from 20,000 to 50,000 feet high)—gave promise of increasing the speed of a plane from 125 to 350 miles per hour. These streams could be used on the west-east trips, since they flow in that direction; they could be avoided on the way back. As much as 40 per cent of the DC-8 flight time is spent in the middle of such air flows.

Long before the DC-8 was chosen by United for its chief carrier, the airline dispatchers and weather experts took on an additional problem. They created a mythical jet-transport plane called "The Ghost" with characteristics much like those of the DC-8. They commenced a regular schedule of nonexistent flights across the country, as they had in Operation Paper Jet.

Flight plans were prepared daily for the Ghost. They were based on the day's weather in the upper altitudes, plus the Ghost's given payloads. Using computers and mathematical calculations based on the plane's configuration, power, size, and weight, they were able to devise methods of tracing the Ghost's progress in its invisible "flight" and to estimate the dangers, difficulties, and advantages right up until the exact landing time.

Thanks to these studies of the Ghost, the operation of a jet transport was understood before the first pilot took the controls. Many of United's findings were incorporated by Douglas into the final model of the DC-8. These included fuel requirements, types of weather, and methods of flight facilitation. The results were so favorable that United and other airlines are continuing just such "paper patrols" in higher and higher altitudes. "We fly it first by a graph on a chart," said one United engineer. "Once we have worn out the points of a dozen pencils, we think we have solved enough puzzles to save maybe a dozen lives in the future." The chief result of these fictitious surveys was that the DC-8 was able to make some of the smoothest, fastest, and most comfortable flights of history—avoiding unfavorable weather and taking advantage of the favorable.

KLM, the Dutch airline, had been doing the same thing for years over the North Atlantic. These results were also available to Douglas to prove the feasibility of the DC-8 to the financial skeptics.

5

Douglas had to assume yet another responsibility: that of the whole, flying airplane. It did not actually manufacture it. The engines, the instruments, and more than 65,000 parts in the plane— some only to be seen by a magnifying glass—were made by subcontractors. If Douglas had actually tried to tool up to manufacture every item that went into a plane, it would have gone collectively insane and probably been sued by the government for monopoly. It had to depend on the building and performance of thousands of other concerns.

In 1957, Douglas did business with more than 11,000 firms, 82 per cent of which were small businesses. The company paid out more than $600,000,000 to firms, 34 per cent directly to small business and the balance to what could be classified as big business. It was difficult to say just how many businesses and suppliers were literally involved in a DC-8 airplane. A single instance would show the difficulty of computing this. The engines on the DC-8 were purchased from Pratt & Whitney, and 50 per cent of the suppliers of this firm were in the small-business field. Figures kept on this relationship since 1954 showed that about 60 cents of the Douglas dollar went to small business.

In order to finance the building of the DC-8, Douglas raised money from every direction. "The loss of the tanker contracts of the Air Force to Boeing was a terrible blow," said one executive. "But it forced us to pare down our thinking. We had to cook or get out of the kitchen."

The money came from bank loans, from the previous profits of Douglas on the sales of the DC-6 and DC-7 families, which were extremely profitable just before the jet age, as well as from funds from two issues of debentures. These, which were actually corporation

IOU's, raised $88,000,000 alone. Into this billion-dollar war chest —which rapidly became depleted as the manufacture of the DC-8 went on—were poured the fat advance payments of the airlines. Douglas contracts required 25 per cent or more in cash on order (50 per cent to foreign airlines), with balance in full at the time of delivery.

The amount of these deposits may be gauged from the fact that, in the fall of 1959, Eastern Air Lines was to try to reduce its original DC-8 order from 20 to 16. Douglas suggested that $575,000 be paid per canceled aircraft; Eastern finally settled for good will and the loss of interest to the amount of $372,000.

A sample of the terms on which the airliners were sold was the deal made with the Japan Air Lines. JAL made a cash payment to Douglas of $7,600,000. Douglas agreed to take $5,700,000 on installments, and the Export-Import Bank loaned JAL $17,200,000 for the rest. The loan was repayable over seven years, beginning in 1961.

Much of this financing had been talked about since 1952. It went into high gear in 1955, when Douglas determined to go ahead. There was little discussion and much agreement among the board of directors with the stand of the Old Man. He had held off until the last moment, despite the pressure of some airlines to have decisions long before, in order to wring all the possible use out of the previous DC models.

By February, 1957, the airlines were committed to buy nearly 400 pure-jet and turboprop craft—at a cost of about two and half billion dollars. More than 200 of these were pure jets. On order were 722 jet airliners. It was a measure of the speed and intensity of the move into the jet field, and the advantages of economy and efficiency. Of the 1,500 airliners then in the sky (the military forces were using 35,000, and private and corporate pilots had 60,000), it was apparent that at least a third were doomed to be retired or sold off.

Once it had decided, Douglas joined the parade to the jets with characteristic vigor and canniness. In 1959, the company reported that one of the major reasons for its decline in earnings (and non-dividends) was the write-off of more than $67,000,000 on the DC-8 program.

But the decision, though conservative, was too late to do much about financing aid to sales. "I've never really known how to sell an airplane before," said Nat Paschall, then vice-president in charge of sales for Douglas. "This time I only had intangibles and a model and blueprints to work with. A model, words, and paper."

6

The most telling argument for financing the DC-8 was that it was the only plane designed from the beginning for people. The competing craft, to a large degree, had been evolved from military experiment. But Douglas, without the backing of tax money, now could make this claim.

One of the chief responses to this need for a "plane for people" was the assignment in 1952 of multiple problems to the Human Factors group of the company. As the co-ordinator, Stanley Lippert, pointed out in 1958, "air conditioning, structures, power plant, interior design, electrical or electronic devices, mechanical controls and acoustics" are traditional in airplane manufacturing, and "human factors problems are inherent in all these fields." This department stepped into the aspects of aircraft design in a wide variety of areas: medical, physiological, psychological, and anthropological. Without usurping the functions of any, they offered usable data in each.

Their findings were largely used in the aeronautical engineering for the first time. In regard to the fear of "explosive decompression" such as had happened to Comet jet transports, it was found that, because of the amount, the 10,000 cubic feet of air in the interior of a DC-8 "cannot flow out of a hole with sufficient speed to create" such an emergency. A hole as big as two square feet at 40,000 feet would take twelve seconds before the whole would decompress. As for "hypoxia," the danger of strangling in the thin upper limits, this appeared to be no danger, even without oxygen. The HF studies showed that "most passengers will descend safely to 14,000 feet—where the air is rich enough in oxygen—even if they have no mask."

As for escape on the ground, three hundred men, women, and children made 12,000 individual exits during a year in order to get the exact needs and dimensions of the final escape hatch. "Beside the effects of dimension and agility," the report said, "comparisons by age, sex, and stature were made."

The original design of the eleven-second flush toilet of Douglas manufacture was preceded by a 1954 study of waste elimination of 256 flights involving more than nine thousand passengers. Even the seat cushions were examined in the light of "local body pressures," applied anthropometry, and materials. It resulted in saving 300 pounds per plane—a value to DC-8 buyers over a ten-year period of millions of dollars.

7

One of the most fascinating HF studies was in regard to animals. Carrying pets and highly bred specimens is a growing part of passenger service. The DC-8 animal compartment is a concession to this trend. A 1957 study was made which exposed animals to simulated DC-8 flying conditions for periods of up to ten hours—including noise and air-pressure effects. It took into account the type and size of the animal, duration of flight, cargo loaded in next-door areas, and the rate of air change. The chief animals used were cats, dogs, monkeys, and birds.

The animals were inspected and certified to be in good health before the experiment. The four-phased investigation was planned in steps. In the first, the animals were put into shipping cages and sealed into sea-level pressure chambers to check their rate of burning up air. The chamber then was subject to the lighter pressure of 8,000 feet of height. Then came a short exposure of 110 decibels.

of jet-engine noise at 8,000 feet. Finally, at the same "height," the animals took ten hours of exposure to continuous jet noise.

It was found that the animals had severe difficulty in breathing with a concentration of 6 per cent carbon dioxide. So the compartment was limited to less than 5 per cent for the end of any flight. A large safety factor was introduced. It was noted that small birds produced more than four times the carbon dioxide of large birds per pound; the same was true of small animals versus big ones. Thus the carrying capacity was set for the maximum and minimum population of the animal world.

It was found that the amount of air available to the animals could vary from 100 to 700 cubic feet, depending on how many of what occupied the space. It was also determined that the animals were entitled to the same cabin altitude as humans—6,700 feet while flying at 40,000 feet, a lower altitude than a steer enjoys in a Denver pasture. The heat from the radio tubes was piped into the bottom of the compartment to keep it between 60 and 90 degrees Fahrenheit. These extremes were acceptable to the animals.

The report pointed out that "easily obtainable mongrels" were not used; instead, they experimented on such sensitive breeds as Chihuahuas, cocker spaniels, and Irish setters; Siamese cats; capuchin and spider monkeys; and large birds such as mynas and parrots and small birds including finches and parakeets. These animals ranged in weight from two hundredths of a pound to forty-three pounds. They were all kept for a two-week period of observation after their "flight." None showed any ill effects.

8

The HF group at Douglas was continuously engaged in one major study and thirty-odd minor studies. "Our job," said Lippert, "is to define contraptions in terms of people." Their major study was anthropometric. In this, they refused to work with averages, preferring extremes; but some idea of the "ideal" airline passenger could be secured from their data. At present, he is male; but in

the near future he may be female, if the ladies continue to fly high
and often. The average weight is about 175 pounds; the average
height is about 5 feet 9 inches with shoes on; and the width at
the shoulders (the key comfort point) is about 18 inches. It was
noticed that the height of airline pilots remained about the same
as that in a 1944 study, but the men were considerably heavier
as of 1950. The Douglas men had also examined reports on African
pygmies and even on freak giants, although there is little business
done with either class by the airlines.

Their anthropometric library had about eight thousand docu-
ments and was one of the best in the world. They had been collect-
ing items for fifteen years and bemoaned the fact that the real
up-to-date studies did not exist. One of the best studies of measure-
ments came from a Japanese document, which examined fifty-one
pilots of an airline several years ago. Their basic find was a study
made of the railroad "traveling public" in 1944. "We find that our
public in the air really tends, more and more, to resemble the
facts in the census," said Lippert.

The HF men tended to agree with a testy airline executive who
criticized some of their findings. "Everyone who has a rear end has
an opinion," he said, "and it's just as hard to change." They felt
that present scientific approaches to making people as comfortable
as gadgets in the air were very meager: "We try to change 90 per
cent guess and 10 per cent knowledge into the other way around."

Their finger seemed to be in every pie. The 147-inch width of the
DC-8 body came from their studies of shoulder width. The cockpit
was arranged on their advice to "hang the pilot from his eyeballs,
since it's primarily a visual problem. We'll bring up the seat under
him." They studied why it is easier for a tall man to slump than for a
small man to reach. They worked three months on things like
human legs in eleven different positions, including knee crossings,
to get the maximal comfort positions. They made "mock-ups of
people" in plastic, to prove their points of weight and room savings.
"We found that adding even an extra inch in the plane beyond

reasonable comfort limits added three hundred pounds to the plane," said Lippert. "We figured that over ten years this would mean a loss of $108,000,000 to an airline with one hundred planes."

Some of their information about the size and weight of the human being (both hands being about three pounds, the head being over twelve and a half pounds) came from a German study of fifteen cadavers and an American dissection of four more. Such studies were required in military-plane designing; but when Lippert and his helpers began, in 1944 at Douglas, there was no such department. Even then, they were not officially recognized until 1948. "We've always been outspoken for the passenger," said Lippert ruefully, "and we've never discovered a device to replace our foot in the mouth."

Knowing that the ear is the center of airsickness and that it is an up-and-down motion, rather than a sideways or rolling motion, that causes it, they were happy with the coming of the jet engines. The piston-engine propeller slugs of air were hitting the fuselage, and the vibration and noise made the passengers unhappy. "We stuffed the rear of the cabin with things that were either stiff, solid, or sound absorbing," said John Roebuck, Lippert's assistant. Even the inside panels of the plane were mounted on rubber to absorb sound.

"It's so easy to complain about our studies," said Lippert. "I can design a perfect chair, for example, and make you uncomfortable with one ten-thousandth of an inch distortion. How about a needle point sticking up through the seat?" One man complained that he had flown so high that he had fallen asleep and contracted some sort of illness, but they found he had actually been flying in an atmosphere that was lower than his home town of Mexico City.

The windows (a five-man-year effort) were designed with HF help, so that passengers could look down rather than out for comfort and so that even three abreast would provide a maximum view for the man farthest inside. They campaigned for the false ceiling in the DC-8 to give a greater sense of a "room." The result gave a secure feeling and left space for storage of water and other items, together with the ducts of the air-conditioning system. They even worked out a graph that showed how far the stewardesses could lean forward with an average loaded tray without falling.

TWELVE:

"WHAT! HOW MUCH?"

1

THERE IS a famous story which, like a few famous stories, is true. In 1955, the year when the pre-production selling of pure-jet transport planes was at its most cutthroat, Douglas took one of his rare trips east. He went to see Captain Eddie Rickenbacker of Eastern Air Lines.

A man of immense energy and foresight, Rickenbacker—as an American hero both in war and peace—is one of the grand old men of aviation. He can be as courteous as a Southern gallant or as crusty as French bread. On this occasion, he had chosen the latter. "I don't want to talk to sales teams any more," he had snapped. "I want to talk to Don!"

The melancholy, precise Douglas went to see him. As a man who expects the worst—he was convinced in 1941 that the Japanese could not be stopped from bombing Los Angeles—Douglas was probably sure that the conference would be a fiasco. But it was a big-order possibility for DC-8's, and Rickenbacker was an old friend.

As Douglas sat down with his experts, Rickenbacker started firing staccato questions at him from a long-prepared list. His own team of experts had dug deep into the vitals of the DC-8 program.

162

He wanted fast, accurate assurances. He wanted them from the top man.

As the questions crackled, Douglas would look sadly at one of his experts, get the answer, and reply. Finally, well down the list, Rickenbacker hit the real poser of them all. "I want a noise level no higher or even less than the DC-7," he said. "Can you guarantee that?"

Douglas' face sagged a little. His sound-suppression expert apprehensively jerked his head toward the door. "I'll have to confer on that," Douglas said to Rickenbacker. The head of Eastern Air Lines nodded. Outside the door, the expert shook his head. "We've made fine progress," he told Douglas, "and the chances are we'll be able to do it by the time the DC-8 is certified for commercial service."

"What about right now?" asked Douglas.

The expert shook his head again. "Right now we can't guarantee it," he said. "But, as I—"

"Let's go back in," Douglas said mournfully. He re-entered the office, where Rickenbacker was waiting expectantly. "Well," asked the toughest man to sell in aviation, "what about it?"

"We can't guarantee it," Douglas said.

Rickenbacker grinned and thrust out his hand. "You've just sold yourself $80,000,000 worth of airplanes!" he cried. "What I'm buying here isn't the DC-8's, it's integrity!"

The meeting broke up. The victorious Douglas forces paraded toward the outer office. "Just the same, Don," Rickenbacker said suddenly. "I hope you're going to keep on working to keep that noise down."

Douglas nodded. "I'll use my integrity," he said solemnly.

2

For as long as Douglas has been in business—the past forty years—he has sold integrity first and airplanes second. Even if he had taken up circus high-diving, he would probably have sold the same thing first. This quality, which he instills into his labor force and executives, is the foremost recommendation of an airplane like the DC-8. "The guy has rubber airplanes," grumble some of the Douglas competitors. "When they want a new model, they just stretch out one of the old ones."

The criticism is true within limits. Raymond's capacity for growth, the insistence of Douglas on a family of planes—they amount to the same thing. They bring to the basic design an inherent factor that cannot be sensed except by those who have known Douglas or flown his planes. It is the single greatest appeal in the selling of any DC craft.

Next, perhaps, is the fact that Douglas stands squarely behind each of its models. The network of technical men and engineers that is stationed all around the world proves it. The modifications that Douglas is willing to make without charge prove it. The voluntary grounding of the planes in an emergency is another proof. So is the continued tradition of Douglas interest in every one of its 30,000 planes, whether flying or grounded.

Rickenbacker was right: he had shaved the Douglas prices by rubbing them against those of Boeing, he had whipsawed one against the other for weeks, and he had finally got what he wanted. Integrity is the wing span of any good business. He had known DC's for the past twenty-two years.

But another airline, even larger than Eastern, did not agree with this conclusion. They figured up the same list as Rickenbacker, and bought differently. According to M. G. Beard, assistant vice-president of American Airlines, in charge of comparing the two models of the Boeing 707 and the DC-8, the choice was rough. Beard explained his position at length:

"It appeared to us at American Airlines . . . that the difficulty with American models in 1952 was that they had too much speed and too little payload." He wanted a reduction of perhaps 50 miles per hour and a boost of 20 more passengers to achieve an economical plane. The American Airlines objections were met eventually by an increased power thrust from 10,000 pounds to 12,500 pounds. This allowed the speed to be kept up while enlarging the plane and taking on more fuel. It was not until 1954 and 1955, Beard felt, that their analysis of military-bomber operations showed that the engine reliability was coming up to the commercial minimum.

So, between 1949 and 1955—between the year of the operation of the first English Comet I and the time when the world airlines really bought jets—the laboratory work got done. "The selection of the right transport to buy," said Beard, "between the Douglas DC-8 and the Boeing 707, was the hardest to make of any I can remember in all the years since 1932." Then American had bought the DC-2. In 1955, they ordered thirty Boeing 707's.

"The airplanes were both excellent in design features. Both mounted the J-57 engine and were about the same size and weight. Both structures were designed for long fatigue life. Both pressure cabins were designed with adequate rip stops to protect against disastrous rapid decompressions, should anything puncture the skin. The speeds were not too far apart. Both cockpits were logically arranged. The economics compared closely. Both companies had the reputation of building good commercial transports. Douglas had a definite edge in customer relationship, but Boeing had a jet transport flying."

It was the first really big decision of the race. The minor skirmishes had been won by Douglas. (In 1955, National Airlines had signified their intention of going all-jet and all-Douglas.) In the other major race, to get the business of Pan American, the canny PA president, Juan Trippe, had split his business right down the middle with both companies.

In 1955, with Douglas not yet having pulled its design together —it was not "jelled," as the engineers say, as against a "fluid" design, which is flexible but set in main points—the big rush of orders to Douglas indicated the remarkable reputation that company had for making airplanes that are reliable and airworthy, even in a new field.

At that time the DC-8 and the 707 were about even except for the wing sweep. In this, Boeing had chosen to go back at a military 35-degree angle. Douglas elected the more stable wing sweep back of 30 degrees. It made the plane easier to handle in the "Dutch rolling" characteristics, in cross-wind take-offs and landings, and in other handling characteristics. But the 35-degree angle gave Boeing more speed with less drag.

"Since the American traveling public is speed conscious and since with the same power plants there would be a speed differential between the two airplanes in favor of the 707, the difference in wing sweep became an important factor to consider," Beard said. American had always felt that the "wing should be matched to the job"—that is, that a big wing, with the resultant fuel expense, should not be used on short hops. Boeing offered two sizes of wing; Douglas would offer only one for both intercontinental and domestic operators. Since, as Beard pointed out, "the wing is the most critical unit of the airplane," American felt that the "annual bill for flying it would be considerable." The final item that influenced American to buy the 707 was that the price in round numbers was about $500,000 less than the DC-8.

3

What had made the American Airlines decision strange to Douglas was the order of C. R. Smith, the president, to switch to another plane. His attitude reflected the sharpness of the competition and the ruthlessness needed to keep alive. He had always been a Douglas partisan: in the years past, he had been the first to switch his entire fleet to the old reliable DC-3. Douglas had always paid tribute to his judgment. He had said that "his tremendous faith in us and in the future of air travel, his boundless energy and clear vision, and his uncanny knack of making and inspiring the right decision at the right time, were the catalytic agents that greatly influenced us in taking the steps to build that famous and historic airplane."

Now it was United Air Lines, the closest competitor of American, which came into the breach. On October 25, 1955, president W. A. Patterson announced that he would spend about $175,000,000 for thirty DC-8's—the largest jet-airliner order yet placed with any manufacturer. He also announced that forty-three DC-6's and -7's, costing more than $64,000,000, had earlier been ordered from Douglas, to backstop the passenger demand until delivery of the DC-8's.

According to Patterson, the reasons for his buying DC-8's were clear, if a little involved. He declared that his engineers had worked with Douglas since 1936, when United bought its first DC-3. "We didn't want to lose twenty-two years of Douglas experience with us and ours with Douglas," he said.

Patterson pointed out that, after he came to United in 1933, he assembled a team of five experts. They put together their ideas for an airplane and had these translated into engineering specifications. With this in hand he went on a tour to find out what he could do for pricing prototypes.

At Douglas he encountered Raymond and presented his list. "I want passenger service and reliability," said Patterson. Raymond was fascinated by his ideas. Douglas, in on the conversation, asked a pertinent question: "Are the other airlines interested?" Patterson confessed that three other rivals felt much the same way he did.

"But to develop this plane is an experimental project. Are you serious?" demanded Raymond. Patterson said he was. The result was the early DC-4.

It was probably that moment which sold the DC-8. Instead of simply evaluating the Douglas prototype, Patterson said, "We took all the Douglas commercial planes and some of his military and put them together as representative of what the DC-8 would be."

Patterson believed that Douglas himself did not know how important he was to his own organization. He pointed out that he was not only an outstanding engineer who never permitted himself to be distracted from his current problems, he was also a man who mediated between manufacturer and customer and never failed to reconcile the two. Added to this was the fact that Douglas could see the hint of a major problem and set about solving it. Finally, Patterson declared, "If someone would come into his office firing a cannon, he would approach it coolly. God gave Scotsmen what he didn't give all of us—a shrewd analytical capacity." Raymond put the Douglas personal sales appeal in another kind of nutshell: "I would say consistency and an almost uncanny ability to give the right answer intuitively."

4

Boeing was able to design and build its air-transport prototype at a cost of $16,000,000 and justify its gamble because of the later military-tanker contracts. But once it had finished its prototype, the design was largely frozen. The business competition became merciless. Boeing flew more than one hundred demonstration missions. It allowed fifty airline and government pilots to slip in behind the controls. Douglas helped United Air Lines build a DC-8 cabin in San Francisco and feverishly showed off its mock-ups and blueprints.

Douglas engineers compared the DC-8 against its predecessor, the DC-6B, until then the most economical transport. The calculations were all in favor of the Eight. Against a 70-mile-per-hour head wind, the lower cost per pound of the DC-8 resulted in a reduction of approximately 40 per cent in transport cost. The reduction in rates from London to New York was approximately 30 per cent. Even down to a range of 600 miles, the DC-8 maintained an economic advantage of 25 per cent.

Discussions seemed endless. Charts, analyses, and statistics were presented to one airline after another. These were reviewed, and then inspection teams sent to the Douglas plant. Other teams contacted the engine manufacturers. Both groups spent weeks commuting between the competing firms, arguing and discussing prices. The manufacturers revised and cut and redesigned to their demands as much as they could. The final discussions (after the letters of intent to buy) went into the details of deliveries, terms, and financing, and had to be blest by the final decision of the airline board of directors.

In spite of Paschall's modest disclaimer, his twenty years with the Douglas company proved out. He had sold nearly a billion and a half dollars' worth of airplanes (in conjunction with his expert technical crews). He was to sell about half a billion more of DC-8's before he retired in 1960.

What he had to work on were the facts that Douglas was tooling up to produce; that it had its needed financial backing; that it could and had produced quality planes for years; and that it would deliver when it said it would. Paschall's cardinal principle was that he had always refused to run down the competition. Now it became an act of supreme will power. He knew Boeing had a plane flying that could perform adequately, was cheaper in price, and could be delivered earlier.

He started out with his teams. They were composed of engineers in the field of power plants, structure, acoustics, and economics—and occasionally lawyers. The sales people spearheaded the advance into the soft underbelly of the customers, hoping that their chief talking point could be merely to point to the long and honorable Douglas reputation. As it was, that was how it turned out. By the spring of 1960, nearly 160 DC-8's had been sold. Said Douglas half seriously to Paschall on this phenomenal showing: "If we had been flying a prototype and been as early as our competition and hadn't shut them out, I'd have fired you."

The sales and financing took months and months. In 1958, Paschall flew over 100,000 miles: "I got so I hated to see the blank face of a suitcase staring up at me." When someone asked him how he liked the job, he said, "It's not a business, it's a disease."

The ironic part of it was that Paschall's stepfather had been Boeing, the founder of the major rival firm. He had named his youngest son, Boeing Paschall, after him. One night during the height of the sales war between Boeing and Douglas, his phone rang. It was a prospective customer.

"Look at the concessions we're getting from Boeing," complained
the caller to the weary Paschall.

"The hell with Boeing!" Paschall exploded. His three-year-old
son looked up from his lap. "Who, me, daddy?" he asked.

5

The tale of the sales can be charted by the early ebb and flow.
In June, 1955, the decision was made to make the DC-8. On
October 13, Pan American ordered twenty-one planes; on October
25, United ordered thirty. On November 7, National Airlines
ordered three and, on November 16, KLM ordered twelve. The
friends of Douglas were beginning to come in. December was
a big month. Eastern ordered sixteen planes, and Japan Air Lines
ordered four five days later. On December 21, Scandinavian Airlines System ordered seven.

In January, 1956, Swissair ordered three. In February, Delta
Air Lines ordered six. In May, Trans-Canada Air Lines ordered
six. And not until June did the construction of the DC-8 assembly
plant begin—and not until February, 1957, was the first assembly
work started. Meanwhile, six more airplanes had been ordered—
by UAT, TAI, and Olympic Airways. The first fuselage and wings
were joined in October—two years after the first order. The next
month, United boosted its order to forty planes.

In March, 1958, Alitalia ordered four; in May, Iberia Air Lines
ordered two more. In December, Northwest Airlines took five and
in April, 1959, the Philippine Airlines ordered two more. But it
was not until June 3, 1959, that Douglas delivered the first DC-8
to United. Once the first one was off the line, the next followed
swiftly twenty days later, on June 23. The big sales advantage of
Boeing was over. The race was on even terms. Everyone could see
and compare for himself on the ground and in the air. The days
of the mock-ups and paper models were over for Douglas sales
teams.

It is only possible to underestimate the number of millions of miles flown by the salesmen, evaluation experts, and executives of the various airlines before any big jet transports were bought. The Douglas plant was invaded by inspectors and visitors. The Douglas salesmen and expertized teams wandered all over Europe and Asia. Paschall made a dozen trips to Montreal alone to sell the DC-8 to a Canadian airline. Energetic and thorough characters like Rickenbacker would spend days on end, from eight in the morning until six at night, quizzing and inspecting. He even sighted down the interior lines of the DC-8 to make sure they were straight. Other executives simply sat in the California sunshine outside the plant for the specific purpose of getting suntans with their DC-8's. At one point the number of potentates arriving at Douglas, Long Beach, was so great that it caused a momentary confusion of protocol. One employee mentioned that Pope John XXIII was leaving Rome. "My God!" cried a panicked Protestant greeter. "Is *he* coming through, too?"

It was a case of comparing endless specifications, of exhibiting testing rigs and models, of asking a stream of questions, and meeting fact head-on with fact. "Will you give on this?" became a perennial question, together with "Can you give us this?" Douglas struggled to keep its profits above water and still satisfy a customer; but no great leeway was available. All had to be satisfied within the general area of a new aircraft in the sky.

One airline executive spent weeks in California and went away mumbling; then, suddenly, one night called up Douglas personally and bought in five seconds. Rickenbacker smacked the table with his fist and stood up and bought. The deal with United, most important of all, seemed to be getting nowhere for six months; then one morning Patterson called Douglas in his office and told him of their decision. A Dutch airline that had always used Douglas planes told the company: "We've gone along with you on the DC-2's, -3's, -4's, -5's, -6's and -7's; we might as well keep on going right up with the numbers."

One line insisted on Rolls-Royce Conway engines. This meant a reconfiguration of the engine pod and a beefing up of structure.

The order did not mean that much in itself, but Douglas took a gamble on getting more orders for that specific engine. It paid off.

The Japanese demanded an interior lounge that looked like a teahouse in the sky—complete with shoji screens, mats, and the various porcelain fittings of the ground version, including a means of making and serving piping-hot tea. An American firm haggled loudly, apparently for form's sake, and then abruptly bought because it wanted to be first with jets on its particular route. Others split their orders; others in the Far East took only two or three planes—"but the negotiators were smarter than a treeful of owls," said Paschall. A Greek airline ordered a number of DC-8's and then tried to cancel out the contract. This failed because of the fore-sighted advance-cash policy of Douglas. This was followed by payments throughout the production of the plane and a final payment on delivery. Occasionally Douglas had to accept paper from such an institution as the Export-Import Bank.

Some airlines, such as a large one in France, had already been tied up by the competition. The same was true of at least one major airline in the United States: "We never had a chance, they wouldn't talk seriously to us," said Paschall. A large South American line bought DC-8's almost immediately. So did some in Asia.

The foreign inspectors and buyers were generally not so fastidious as the American. The great problem was allaying the "Comet fear," the anxiety over the "explosive decompression" of that plane years before. Douglas, with the best history in the industry on plane fatigue and safety, was able to use its reputation to counter the phobia.

"It was a neck-and-neck affair all the way along," said Paschall. "But none of us thought for a moment that we'd lose it."

6

The only contact most people have with a plane is by the seat of their pants. They bet their bottom dollar on passage. With this for a measure, the Douglas specialists, as far back as the beginning of the secret DC-8 special project in 1952, had projected their statistics into the future. They had discovered that the 1965 air traffic might amount to as much as 41,000,000,000 passenger-miles—roughly double that proved to exist by 1956.

The prospects for the future seemed to be virtually unlimited. Birth rates were rising, and more travelers in the sub-$10,000-per-year income bracket were taking to the air. Finally, the pattern of growth fitted into the past history of aviation progress from 1933 to 1941.

One of the big sales arguments for the DC-8 was that although it cost more than twice as much as the $2,000,000 DC-7, it was expected to produce two to three times as much revenue for the airline as its sister plane. Not only that, the Eight was set up for an estimated minimum of ten years of service—as opposed to the DC-7's seven-year span.

As for payload, the DC-8 needed at least a ton per passenger to make a trip. The goal of the honeybee remained the ultimate: to carry its own weight in nectar. But the airlines, which had, as Patterson put it, "translated ideas into engineering specifications and then went in search of price quotations," appeared satisfied. By 1960, the jet transport had come of age in the estimate of all concerned. The advent of such speed and comfort had caught the fancy of all commercial operators. Many ordered jets immediately. (About 230 of the craft were expected to be delivered in 1960-61.)

7

The big problem was for the major airlines to find some spot to get rid of their fleet of once-cherished, now surplus four-motored piston-engine craft. There had been no difficulty in the past in selling such obsolescent planes. They could be bargain-priced to non-scheduled lines, feeder lines, or cargo operators, or even shipped abroad. Now the customers were wary, or they had already committed themselves to the new style. The piston-engine jobs were assigned to cargo or leasing or charter, or put into the tourist trade with high-density passenger seating. Some were turned back to the manufacturers. Still others simply depreciated as tax write-offs.

It was a stymied position for Douglas and all the rest. The financial problem was with the industry to stay. Douglas was thinking not only of making money in the long haul but of getting out of the bind of the present.

The selling ideas of the DC-8 dated back almost to 1950. Douglas had encountered opposition to his ideas before. He was one of the first converts to the now common practice of flying land planes over the oceans. He expressed his belief that they could operate over water with more efficiency and as much safety. The military had given him very little support and a great deal of opposition. Nevertheless, he had gone ahead on his own to create the DC series and shift the ponderous thinking of the bureaucrats in the days before World War II. The same stubborn vision led him to the DC-8 despite the competition and the lack of government enthusiasm.

By July, 1956, the race for the jet-transport business had narrowed down. Boeing, which had flown its prototype across the country in four and a half hours, had promised its first for December, 1958. It also promised a larger intercontinental job for August, 1959. It told of orders for eighty-eight of the two types of the 707. Douglas, on the strength of blueprints alone and the reputation of the company, told of eleven airlines ordering 114 DC-8's. "We're not building a prototype yet," he said shortly, "but each part was severely tested three years ago." He added that the company had invested $140,000,000 so far and would put out its version for the race first (domestic) in 1959 and the intercontinental long-range model in 1960.

None of the American manufacturers thought too much of the competition from abroad. The first crashes of the English Comet I in 1952 had taken much of the gimp out of their plans. Their Comet II, after extensive retesting, had been launched by 1956, and the Russians had their own uncomfortable version of a jet liner in the air for several months. "Actually, Russia's competition scared us then more than any other," said a Douglas spokesman. "We examined the plans for the early British planes and had no confidence in their kind of construction. We tried to warn them. The English don't listen very well."

What turned out to be the genuine European contribution came from France. *Sud Aviation* produced the sleek jet Caravelle with the engines located far back near the tail. Douglas test pilots went over to inspect it in 1959. They flew it carefully a dozen times. The DC-9 project was shelved on the strength of their recommendations.

Instead, Douglas plumped for selling the *Sud Aviation* Caravelle, an 85-passenger, twin jet, short-to-medium-range aircraft of France. Douglas took over the market in the western hemisphere and, according to the president, "when sufficient orders are received, we intend manufacturing the Caravelle in this country."

THIRTEEN:

THE DESIRABLE DELAY

1

DURING one of his first sailing races—on Long Island Sound—young Donald Douglas hit a snag. He tore a jagged hole in the side of his small craft. After he had finished the race, a long way behind the last, he came sluggishly in to the dock. His mother saw what had happened.

"Why didn't you come in right away?" she asked him.

"Mother!" said Douglas reprovingly. "When you go into a race, you have to finish it."

Some forty-five years later, Douglas faced the same situation—this time the major crisis of his life. The manufacturing of aircraft, always a neck-and-neck race, had become ruthless. Aeronautical design had become fined down to the point where merely the most technical details or a few pounds or miles per hour could win or lose a sales contract.

In this instance the race was between Douglas and the Boeing Aircraft Company of Seattle, Washington. Owing to its military contracts and its canny, calculated gamble of making not only jet bombers but also jet refueling tankers for the United States Air Force—something Douglas had yearned to do—Boeing had managed to get into a commanding technological position. Military experimentation had always led the way for commercial development. Douglas had said himself: "If it were not for the military expenditures, commercial aircraft would cost more than twice as much, would be less advanced, and would cost more to operate."

Boeing had the military edge. It had had intensive experience with jet engines and the aircraft modifications that were part of their use. Not that Douglas was without such experience; but Boeing had been able to work with such planes in the air—the ultimate place of testing in the rapidly developing techniques. In addition, in the building of the Strategic Air Command refueling tanker, the KC-135, they had their rough prototype of what was later to become the 707 commercial jet.

This manufacturing lead enabled them to commence building the pure-jet transport in 1954. They could deliver the perfected and certified commercial product in December, 1958. They announced that they would deliver an even larger jet for intercontinental traffic in August, 1959.

In 1956, at the time that Boeing triumphantly announced these delivery dates, Douglas had no more than a set of blueprints and its reputation and factories. No prototype delivery could be offered until the fall of 1959, nearly a year later. In the hot competition that existed for the limited number of these six-million-dollar products, a year appeared to be a fatal delay. Douglas was in a race, and he knew no other way to operate than to finish it.

The original DC-8 had been announced in the spring of 1955. From tip to tail, it had a length of 140 feet, 6 inches; it had a wing span of 134 feet, 6 inches. It stood 40 feet, 2 inches high, and was powered by four 10,000-pound-thrust J57 jet engines. A year later, the furiously working Douglas engineers—measuring against the specifications of the 707—were able to announce a refined version. It had a length of 148 feet, 10 inches; a wing span of 139 feet, 9 inches. It stood about as high as before, but it had radically increased the power of its engines (J57, J75, and Conway). In 1960, the continually evolving DC-8 was again changed. This time it was 150 feet, 6 inches long, with a wing span of 142 feet, 5 inches.

In March, 1958, two localized opinions were available to the curious about the Douglas-Boeing race. Said the philosophically pessimistic Douglas, "Boeing has an advantage of one year, but in the long run, it doesn't matter." In more specific language, Raymond declared, "Boeing is flying two of its smaller-powered jets and has three more ready. We seem to be behind. Our first flight has yet to be made. However, we feel that on the larger planes our schedule and theirs are about identical. We may even be a month ahead." Whatever the status of the affair, by the summer of 1956, eleven airlines had ordered 123 DC-8 transports.

2

The aircraft-manufacturing group of pioneers is a tightly knit sector of American industry. They know very well what they are doing and what they can expect of their rivals. Douglas himself had always been frank to admit that Boeing was first in the field that he had later pre-empted. He admitted that the DC-8 might never have come into existence for the prime carrier it is, if it were not for Boeing.

Speaking of the year 1931, Douglas said, "We had been designing for the Army and Navy, a few amphibians for millionaire sportsmen, and some open-cockpit biplanes for airmail operators. We had never tackled a passenger plane." But when the Boeing 247 appeared as a specific design for the Boeing-affiliated National Air Transport, TWA sought out a rival plane. The DC-1 was born. (NAT later became United, which, in a mild irony, bought most of the first DC-8's in 1955.)

Thus this fact of being second at the start of a race in the building of a major transport plane did not panic Douglas. It had happened before from the beginning of the DC-series. Additional time gave the maker more room for testing and perfecting. Another major advantage was the speed with which the "state of the art" of aeronautics, especially the power plants, was advancing. Every twenty-four hours saw some new knowledge or desirable refinement coming into being. The runner-up had the opportunity to build better air-planes with later and more efficient devices. Boeing found this out when, in January, 1960, BOAC could not get its fifteen 707's certified by the British government. The newspapers reported that "concern has been caused by two accidents and a serious incident, in all of which 707's have rolled violently in the air. . . . In February last year, near Paris, two engines were thrown off during a violent roll. With remarkable skill the pilot landed the plane safely. At Long Island in August, another 707 on a training flight made a similar violent maneuver at comparatively low height. The plane rolled suddenly and struck the ground. The crew of five, the only occupants, were killed. Near Seattle . . . three engines were thrown off a 707 during a violent roll on another training flight. There also, the instructor pilot made a remarkable landing. He lost his life but saved four others. There have been other similar incidents when only prompt action by an experienced pilot has averted an accident."

In an air directive the October before, the FAA had pointed out that, in the 707, "when yaw angles in excess of approximately ten degrees are attained, the rudder effectiveness deteriorates quite rapidly with a resultant loss of aircraft directional control. Several incidents have shown that this can produce a dangerous flight condition," and proceeded to demand corrective measures. The 707 was also plagued about the same time by a rash of hydraulic failures, thirty-one of them alone in the landing gear. Modifications to improve these and both the high-speed and low-speed characteristics were promptly initiated—at a cost of more than $1,000,000 per plane. Pilots called the 707 a "good" plane but preferred the "fantastically good" low-speed flying abilities of the DC-8 and the doubling up of mechanical systems with manual systems.

Douglas, which had put the Eight into operation without an accident, crossed its fingers. Its most persistent problem came in the spring of 1960. Although the DC-8 had lived up to its "specs" as well as any jet transport, it gulped too much fuel. Engineers set about reducing the drag and improving its lines.

Perhaps Douglas had learned more thoroughly than Boeing that easy does it. The critical point of any decision in the field of making planes is the determination of the time when designs must be frozen as far as possible, even with the inevitable hedgings to incorporate future developments. Such a decision must also take into account the fact that the new and different enjoys a vogue in this country. Public favor generally turns toward the newest and most advanced models. The purchase of the first jets, for example, almost forced the competing lines to require delivery from the plane manufacturers under penalty of losing hundreds of millions of dollars in cargo and passenger revenue.

Nevertheless, said Patterson, speaking for United, "We were glad we waited for the DC-8." When the first certificated DC-8 was delivered in September, 1959, Douglas added: "In ten years the delay will make no difference." Said an executive of a Scandinavian airline: "In ten years we'll be very glad we're flying a Douglas plane."

3

Before all, the will and desire existed. After these came the idea, moving dimly in an abysm of ordered facts. But before the airplane, there was the word; and the word came from Douglas.

After the permissive grunt in 1955, the proposed DC-8 with its engineering release followed a well-marked routine. The decision funneled down through the hierarchy of vice-presidents and commenced a two-pronged route.

The first took it to the chief engineer and on to the advanced design section—aerodynamics, wind tunnels, model design, configuration—and moved to the project engineers and the model shop. From there it was routed into the blueprint stage (it was estimated that the blueprints for the DC-8 model covered roughly four square miles). The master layout was begun.

Meanwhile, the works manager alerted his tooling assistants, as

Donald W. Douglas, Sr., and Donald W. Douglas, Jr.

Donald W. Douglas, Sr. (*left*), delivers flight log and keys to first United Air Lines' DC-8 to UAL President W. A. Patterson.

Captain E. V. Rickenbacker, of Eastern Air Lines, and Frank Boyer, manager of Douglas flight operations at Long Beach.

The DC-8 taking off . . .

. . . in flight . . .

. . . landing.

The DC-8.

An Army Air Force C-47 troop and cargo carrier.

A Douglas "Skymaster" Army C54 combat transport.

The B-19 was the forerunner of America's long-range strategic bombers.

The versatile B-66 tactical bomber.

An AD-5 Skyraider.

An F4D Skyray, first of the modern delta-type supersonic jets.

An A4D Skyhawk, America's smallest and lightest jet combat airplane.

The D-558-2 Skyrocket was the first aircraft to exceed Mach 2, or twice the speed of sound.

A Douglas X-3 high-speed research aircraft.

Donald W. Douglas, Sr., on his first DC-8 ride (1959) (*above*).

KLM
Alitalia
Trans-Canada Air Lines
Swissair
all fly DC-8's.

well as the manufacturing controls manager, the plant superintendent, chief inspector, and chief of matériel. The final master layout was worked out between the planning desk and the layout men, and the work on templates and tool design was commenced. Plaster patterns were poured to molds correct to within one five-thousandth of an inch; jigs and fixtures were created. (These cast-off, fossil remains of the DC-8 could be seen stacked in the rear of the plant years later.)

Production control was also active, funneling its demands through matériel needs into fabrication, minor assemblies, stock rooms, and spares, and finally into the actual assembly line. The engineering department joined with the test department to check the final result after the assembly inspection. The government and airline officials, present at virtually every stage along the line, made intensive surveys of each item and the finished whole.

In the final stages the craft had its numerous flight tests, its FAA government accreditation, its customer acceptance, and went out to become a successful commercial operational aircraft. It had with it, moreover, the blessings of the Douglas plant in the form of spare parts in the field and the technical representatives to take care of all complaints or bugs that might appear in use.

4

The DC-8 was built in Long Beach, California. A special $20,000,000 building—the first in the world for commercial jet manufacture—was erected on twenty-six acres. Most of it was contained in two huge assembly lines: one for structural assembly, the other for final assembly. There were three smaller service buildings, a paint building big enough to cover the whole of one of the massive airliners, and a wing-tanks sealing booth. The largest building was nearly 1,150 feet long and 480 feet wide. "The building was tailored to the plane like a suit to a man," said D. H. Voss, the general superintendent of the facility. "We wanted to be sure we wouldn't be cramped."

The Douglas division at Long Beach, sister to that at Santa Monica, had been established in 1941. It was incorporated originally as an earnest of the Douglas desire to implement the concept of President Franklin D. Roosevelt to make the United States the arsenal of democracy. In November, the plant began operations; on December 7, the Japanese bombed Pearl Harbor. On December 23, the first airplane from the plant was delivered to the Air Force —a DC-3 (C-47), the first of 4,285 C-47's to be made. It also produced 999 A-20 attack bombers, 1,156 A-26 attack bombers, and 3,000 B-17's from the Boeing prototype. What is significant in this record is that, using pounds of airplanes as a standard, Long Beach had the greatest single output of any aircraft plant in the world.

After the basic design of the DC-8 became firm late in 1955, the mock-up work was completed, the tools and forms made, and the final work done before the beginning of fabrication of parts in September, 1956. The assembly commenced at Long Beach in February, 1957.

The mock-up that was finally approved showed that at that time the pressurized portion of the fuselage would be 12 feet wide, 13.5 feet deep, and 115 feet long. Each 40 inches of cabin length could take loads of 1,500 pounds. Ultimate crash loads were designed for nine times the weight of gravity.

The forward compartment would be able to take 6,900 pounds, and the after compartment 7,000 pounds. Although the windows were larger and more "scenic," they were fewer (at 40-inch intervals) because of the weight and safety penalty. Each window was made of triple panes, each a half-inch thick. Overstrength and maximum fatigue resistance, although not all required by the inspectors, were all built into the DC-8.

Titanium was used because it is both light and strong to prevent a defect from spreading, but very little magnesium was employed. Douglas felt it was both a corrosion and a fire problem. (The engine pods were designed to seal off any engine fires. Titanium was used liberally—1,700 separate parts—to guarantee this.) The remarkable skin of the plane was formed out of a war-developed alloy of aluminum. It was made up percentage-wise of 1.6 copper, 2.5 magnesium, 5.6 zinc, and .3 chromium, the rest being pure aluminum. A half-ton of the superstrong titanium was built into each airframe of the DC-8. It saved weight equal to five passengers and their luggage for each flight. At the cheapest this would be equal to a weight saving of a half-ton of cargo, which at mail rates would be a potential earning of $525 for each flight coast-to-coast.

The basic theory of the whole construction was one that was startling in its simplicity. It was the "damn-sure" fail-safe idea.

5

A fail-safe structure is one so arranged that even though a major part of it may be damaged or broken, the airplane itself—with passengers and crew—can land safely. It is designed in four different ways: (1) "multiple structure" uses a large number of members to share a specified load; (2) "double structure" uses two small members in place of one large one; (3) "back-up structure" is that type where one member carries all the load but another stands by to take over in the event of failure; (4) "warning structure" is that kind which is designed to have a stronger member take over when another part of the structure starts to yield.

In the construction of the DC-8 these four types of fail-safe building are shown in the wing three-spar construction, in two-bolt fittings of the fuselage, in the double keel under the landing-gear door or in the passenger-window design. In the latter case, the pressure load is carried on one pane, with a safety factor of eight. If one of these fails, there are two others with the same strength. Breakage has happened perhaps a dozen times in the history of such windows, but only one pane has suffered. In the skin bracing of the plane, each stringer is individual. A crack or break in one will be confined to that particular part.

The floor design of the DC-8 is a good example of multiple structure. High pressure loads are resisted chiefly by the floor beams. If one of these fails, a 40-inch-deep beam along the fuselage transfers the load to adjacent braces with practically no loss of strength. The joint of the skin and frame is a demonstration of warning structure. If a crack begins in the skin, owing to fatigue, and grows because of pressure, the skin automatically transfers its load to the stiff frame on either side of the crack, which halts it on the spot.

A spectacular example of a "safe failure" happened to an American Airlines Douglas plane. A propeller blade flew off. It sheared a huge hole in the top of the cabin. Instead of the fuselage breaking in two, as might have happened, the lost girder was replaced by the side girders carrying the load in an unaccustomed but adequate manner. The airplane landed successfully. (Skin cracks have occurred only twice on the DC-6, but the stresses have been duplicated hundreds of times in tests on the DC-8. In no case did the crack grow past the bracing structure.)

A case of spar failure happened to a DC-6 during a storm on a scheduled airline flight. It lost one of its spar caps. One of the spars collapsed in the wing. The plane continued its flight in extreme turbulence for over an hour and landed safely. Not even the nature of the damage was known until after the landing. Even faced with such a loss, the wing still had a safety factor of two.

6

The years of study that preceded the construction of the big plane were unique in one sense: Douglas trusted Douglas enough to finish the job without a tested prototype. The tests went on with the first ones produced—while operations were under way to build number fourteen of the same model.

Three versions of the transport were made. They were much the same in dimension but used for domestic, intercontinental, and extended range. The last two had heavier skins and stronger frames in order to hold more fuel and carry more weight.

As always, the wing came in for special study: this time the major research was directed toward making a better joining of the wing root to the fuselage.

In order to create the DC-8, the Douglas engineers were required to invent not only the plane itself but also parts of the basic machinery to make it. One of these was a $750,000 four-way stretch press. The company engineers developed the design for the machine. It was built in four months, a third of the time normally needed. Such a press was able to exert pressures as high as 1,200 tons in order to stretch and form the aluminum for the inner skins of the DC-8 wing.

These wing skins were among the largest sheets of that gauge of aluminum ever rolled—averaging more than 10 feet wide by 46 feet long and weighing 1,250 pounds. There was a good deal of danger of injury in unloading and handling. In order to do this with minimum hazard, a vacuum lifting device—32 vacuum cups, 6 inches in diameter, which could raise 10,800 pounds horizontally —was devised.

Another danger appeared in the potential aging of the aluminum. The alloy slowly gets harder and stronger owing to the changes in crystal structure that take place at room temperature. It is a useful shift, since it has a peculiar property of toughening without tempering. Aluminum rivets, for example, become stronger after they are driven. Nevertheless, such a quality makes the material difficult to machine and shape.

To insure that the supplies of aluminum would not become unduly aged before their time, the sheets were shipped in dry ice from the manufacturing plant in Iowa. Upon arrival they were stuffed into a giant deep-freeze, 48 feet long by 12 feet wide by 5 feet deep, where they were kept at −30° until used. Once they were shaped, the wings were aged in an oven with temperatures similar to that of a home kitchen—150° to 450°.

In shaping, the inner skins were removed from the icebox one by one, placed on a padded table, and sawed into rough shape. Dies were first used to shape much of the eight formed-wing skins required for the wings of a single DC-8.

The final forming of the skin section took place in the four-way stretch press. Then after trueing the edges of the wing sheet and oven aging, the wing was chemically cleaned and anodized preparatory to assembly. The wing skin came out, in the final product, as a single structure without a splice, thus gaining all the inherent strength and smoothness of such a design and avoiding the weight of splicing or bolting or riveting.

The thickness of the wing was a major consideration. It had to be deep enough to carry a large amount of fuel, but thin enough to cut through the air with maximum efficiency. The conservative swept-back attachment to the fuselage was primarily due to Douglas, who had worked on the problem as long ago as 1916. (More than a 30-degree angle back from the fuselage, he knew, resulted in the "Dutch roll," which he had described as "a skid followed by a roll with continued yawing and rolling from side to side in corkscrew fashion.")

The wings underwent their own special testing tortures. Hydraulic jacks were set to work at a safe distance by crews with systems of cables. The whole plane was lifted free of the floor to simulate actual flight. Weights spotted inside the fuselage were introduced to counteract upward forces. Hydraulic struts, under regulated pressure, imitated the loads that the engines would put on the wings. The fuel tanks were pressurized to combine the gross effects of pressure with the tests upon the wing proper.

To measure the results of the ultimate investigation, the wing was covered with 800 strain gauges. These could measure the exact stress on it. Other instruments were located so as to measure deflection all along the wing—down to the ultimate thousandth of an inch.

The final and most brutal test came when the jacks boosted the wings of the DC-8 slowly upward, inch by inch. More than 462,000 pounds were applied to each wing tip, about 231 tons on each side. This meant that the wings were taking a stress that would be roughly equal to eleven times the amount expected in routine flights, and with extreme emergencies.

The wing was raised 67 inches by this terrific pressure on each end, bending like a bow. It was bent down slowly in the same manner. It was discovered that the wing could "flap" about nine feet without any particular defects showing—and return to a perfectly normal angle. No injuries were visible. Nor did the extensive investigations of the wing later, with instruments as far removed as the microscope and X-ray, reveal any faults caused by the tests.

7

The Pratt & Whitney engines on the DC-8 were forced to undergo the most intensive tests ever scheduled for an engine. For six months there were lengthy performance tests under normal conditions. The compressor and turbine discs were deliberately overspeeded hundreds of times. Contaminated fuel was injected into the motor. For protracted periods the engines were operated at maximum power and deliberately overheated. Added to these were tests for internal durability. Dozens of foreign objects—including rocks, ice, wrenches, and lunch pails—were forced into the air inlets. As a final check each engine was totally disassembled and each part subjected to thorough scientific inspection.

During this abuse for proof of virtual indestructibility, the first major subcontract was let by Douglas. It went to the Ryan Aeronautical Company—a $20,000,000 document under which Ryan agreed to build the jet pods and pylons to fit the J-57 Pratt & Whitney engines for the DC-8. It was implemented by the arrival of a staff of thirty-five Ryan jet engineers at the Douglas Santa Monica plant to get the designing and adaptation under way.

Meanwhile, in the master pattern section of the plant at Long Beach, the craftsmen were completing shapes that would be accurate to one five-thousandth of an inch to form the metals of the DC-8. The interior-design section was busy in another division of the company, testing more than thirty materials in a five-month run for flammability, wear, strength, and fading. The models for the exclusive seat were being kept more secret than any other single item—a chore that Douglas found congenial, since it had built its own airplane seats for more than twenty-seven years.

Tests went forward on the unique DC-8 duplicate "one-member-out" system. It meant that everything vital on the plane had a duplicate—so arranged that if one failed, the other took over. Most of them were automatic. Its intricate double system of electrical components was to prove so foolproof that Pan American would attempt to persuade Douglas to modify it so that they could install it on their Boeing 707's. Structural test programs began with examples of single simple fastenings; they continued through a succession of large and complex fittings which were similarly tried. The parts having been proved, the whole underwent its own testing. In order to keep the latest developments in the field co-ordinated, research and development groups were ordered to work in close daily contact with the engineers. "Sometimes we interfered with each other, but the effort was worth it," said one.

The forward section of the DC-8 fuselage was specially chosen for testing. There was a valid reason. This section necessarily is built of the thinnest aluminum skin; it also has the largest variety of body openings. Moreover, the structural outline of the cockpit becomes irregular, shifting from the ideal oval cross-section of the other areas. The engineers felt that this particular spot would produce the most violent distortions and bending stresses.

Each cockpit interior commenced to have a different design. Out of seventeen different airlines, seventeen wanted a specially designed cockpit for their pilots. The special installations, however, were all included. They comprised a weather radar installation with a 30-inch antenna that could give an 180-degree horizontal full-beam scan for early warning of storms, turbulences, other planes, or similar navigational dangers. A new and ingenious gimmick appeared—the "foot thumper." It was an electronic sensing device which was built into the rudder pedals. If one of the main landing-gear wheels slipped on an icy runway, the pedals would rap sharply against the pilot's feet. It warned him to let up on the brake pressure. Another device, the DME (Distance Measuring Equipment), was installed to click off the miles like an automobile odometer, computing approach or departure over a ground station with great accuracy.

8

The pressurizing and air conditioning of the DC-8 cabin came in for as much careful attention as the all-important wing. Each was vital to the plane's survival. It was finally worked out so that the passengers and crew—and the animals—at a height of 23,000 feet would have a pressure less than that upon a car driver going from Los Angeles to Death Valley. As for the rate of change experienced by DC-8 passengers, it was reckoned to be less than five feet per second—about a quarter as fast as that in modern high-speed elevators.

In case of damage to one small section of the cabin, it was made positive that the hole could not magnify and rip. The Eight was made so that it could take an escape of air at as much as 350 cubic feet per second and fly without significant discomfort to the human or animal load—and this despite the total load of 5,700,000 pounds on the DC-8 fuselage, distributed over approximately 4,500 square feet.

Douglas put all its extensive studies on riveting and bolting—extending back over dozens of years—into the DC-8. In the past this made up one of the weakest parts of a transport. Now, with "dimpling" holes instead of countersinking, keeping the thickness of the metal, using huck bolts that almost welded the parts together without sacrificing strength or aerodynamic integrity, the rivets actually became strength components. They were aligned so carefully that in a row of one hundred rivet holes a fiftieth-of-an-inch deviation was impermissible.

The aluminum was often protected by what looked like tough paper sheeting. This was to help prevent scratching of the metal. A deep scratch, of course, is an invitation to weakness in the air. But even a shallow one, it has been found, may produce erosion by electrolysis with the moisture in the atmosphere. Welding and riveting were done with the greatest care. A spot of grease will weaken a weld; a rivet awry will cause a deterioration of the joint.

The whole was checked continuously by fine optical tooling, even to the extent of using television devices. The wing spars were built with the same care—because in addition to being the heart of the wing structure, they were also sizable fuel tanks. A movable mechanical riveter was devised to make sure of efficient riveting and to eliminate careless work. In many cases adhesive bonding was employed.

The rivet holes were the subject of intensive investigation. Since they are potentially hundreds of thousands of sources of trouble, they were drilled to the microscopic tolerance of five ten-thousandths of an inch, and each hole inspected more than a dozen times before and after the "shaving of their heads."

9

While these simultaneous operations were justifying the Douglas labor force, the plane itself was taking shape in the middle of the million-square-foot Long Beach plant—a spot big enough for eighteen football games to be played at the same time. The raw interior of the fuselage, filled with the bright Gothic arches of frames and stringers, looked like a small modern cathedral.

The seats were engineered to stand up to 133 per cent more of a crash load than would crumple the plane itself. The belts were built to withstand a dozen times the force of gravity. Since two superchargers were minimum equipment, Douglas installed four. The exhaust of heated cabin air was picked up and used to run turbo-compressors. These gave about 220 horsepower, about ten of them being due solely to the body heat of the passengers. "I don't suppose they'll ever know that they're adding about six or seven miles to the speed of the plane and partly working their way," observed a technician.

A vapor cycle system was set up to condense the humidity into large drops, trap it, and drain it overboard. Tests proved that the insulation of the cabin was enough to keep it at 75° while the temperature outside went down to −100° and up to +120°.

Knowing from experience that parts that do not quite quite fit and must be jammed together become a major source of flaws, technicians checked them at every interface and bolthole. Aware of the principle that the stress is greater in big sheets than small ones, Douglas engineers plumped for the more expensive procedure of putting together assemblies of small pieces. Instead of splicing or fastening just where the body of the cabin joined the wing— the point of heaviest stress in any plane—Douglas formed 47-foot-long sections to fit the bend. It was a joint that was ten times as fatigue resistant as those used before.

The DC-8 assembly line had thirteen stages—a dozen inside the main building and one outside—where a pressure check was run on each fuselage before it was joined to the tail and cockpit. Although the Eight was a totally new plane, the methods of construction used in the DC-6 and the DC-7 series were used. The wings were sealed inside by special coatings and checked for leaks by a "soap-bubble" technique.

Before the first ceremonious wing joining, 123 DC-8's had been ordered sight unseen by fourteen of the world's airlines. The joining itself was a symbolic fifteen-minute job that was done exactly on schedule—the schedule that had been set up three years before.

The 19,000-pound fuselage, shining and scrubbed, was slung into position. The right- and left-wing units, joined carefully to make a single 136-foot wing, were juxtaposed and lapped. Then the 27,000-pound span was moved underneath the big window-pocked fuselage. It was carefully brought into alignment. A system of slings lowered it so gradually that micrometers could be used to caliper the descent.

Moving into final assembly, the DC-8 was minus engine pods and the very tips of its being. The wings were cut short; the tail and nose were cropped. Work moved out from the heart of the wing joining, in a steady progression, out to the extremes of the craft.

The three-point ten-wheel landing gear on which the DC-8 stood was notable for the castered design. They let the big plane turn in a radius of one inch—plus 91 feet. (The DC-7C took 81 feet for clearance of the wing tips.) They carried it to the instrumentation center, to the final check points.

This far along the road to completion, the first DC-8 ever built was ready to take to the air. "We were 99 per cent sure she would fly," said Heinie Heimerdinger, assistant chief pilot in charge of the DC-8 program. "It was only the one per cent that had us all worried."

FOURTEEN:

HOW HIGH, HOW FAST?

1

THE BODY dropped from about 12,000 feet. It curled over in a dive, the arms and legs flopping aimlessly about. "It didn't open!" squawked the voice from the chase plane behind the testing DC-8. "The parachute didn't open!"

The body continued its long, graceful arc. It ended abruptly in the alkali sands of the desert surrounding Edwards Air Force Base. A cloud of dust obscured it as a group of people ran toward the spot. "Poor Sad Sam," mourned one. "He got it at last."

Sad Sam was disintegrated. His iron skeleton, his two hundred pounds of solid limbs, his equipment from oxygen mask to helmet, all were hopelessly ruined. As the official dummy for the DC-8 escape tests, he would fly no more.

"Do you know," joked Heimerdinger, "that three engineers got sick and quit on us that day?"

It was only one of the innumerable tests that the DC-8 had to go through before it satisfied Douglas and its FAA certifiers. It was a dropout to prove that a test crew could escape from the big plane in case of malfunction. In commercial flying, no member of the crew would abandon a plane in case of disaster until all the passengers had cleared. Clearing the passengers by parachute—all

193

150 of them, in time—is so impractical that no commercial transport carries a single one. Nor is this the only reason: the jet vehicles have proved so reliable and the emergency-landing procedures efficient enough, by dint of long testing, that they are not needed. In all the commercial-plane accidents in the world during the past few years, it is doubtful if a half-dozen people would have been saved by parachutes.

This was one of the many conclusions worked out by flight testing of such planes as the DC-8. The pilots put the Big Eight—flatly identified in the semiconfidential flight-training manual issued for the forty-six test pilots of Douglas as a "trans-sonic" creation—through new and old stunts. They were lengthier and more scrupulous than previously conducted examinations in the air. More was known, and more had to be found out.

2

At the Long Beach plant, eleven months and a day after the first DC-8 had begun, the eleventh DC-8 had been begun and the wing and fuselage of the third plane had been joined. The first plane had been totally assembled and was undergoing ground and instrumentation checks. The second was 90 per cent complete.

On April 9, 1958, the first "roll-out" of the DC-8 occurred. The ship was a gleaming white with red-and-blue trim. It was nearly ready to go. Proof tests of its flight-control system were completed. It needed only final inspection and tuning up for its take-off.

On May 30, 1958, the "Gentle Jet," as it was to be called—with its shell-like engine pods and slim retreating wings, with its towering tail and tall landing gear—managed to look massive and frail at the same moment. It had a short five-minute preflight checkup. Then, at 50,000-pound thrust, loaded to 197,000 pounds with water ballast, it ran 3,250 feet to get a take-off speed of 147 miles per hour and roared blackly into the sky and out of sight over the Pacific Ocean.

An audience of 95,000 people—most of them Douglas employees and friends—watched the DC-8 maiden flight. No more than 50,000 visitors had been expected, but the first-flight adventure was too much to stay away from. What made it all the more impressive was that the workers voluntarily gave up their Memorial Day holiday to attend. The DC-8 carried up with it their hopes and fears for the future.

The confidence of the makers and pilots was astounding in its nonchalance. The aplomb of Douglas and its faith in the DC-8 could be guessed by the fact that three months before the plane flew, a flight schedule was put out announcing the take-off time as 10 A.M., May 30, 1958. An English aviation expert, attending the ceremony, remarked that this was the first time such a cocksure pronouncement had ever been made for a prototype plane. "You Douglas chaps certainly do things up brown," he said brightly. "Nothing at all left to chance, eh?"

Actually, the DC-8 did not take off until 10:10 A.M. At the schedule moment the sky was heavily overcast. After the ten-minute delay the crew was ordered to take off regardless of the haze. Some benign celestial influence dissipated the mists just before the Eight reached them.

The first flight was for two hours out over the ocean and back (on a carefully charted course) over uninhabited areas, to Edwards Air Force Base, a United States Air Force test center in the desert about one hundred air-miles from the coast. The Air Force allowed Douglas to have two fighter planes to trail the DC-8 as "chasers" to detect any test failures. The over-ocean test was flown until the crew deemed the plane absolutely normal in operation. In spite of all this "confidence" on the part of Douglas, there were explicit instructions, an escape hatch and parachutes, and a half-dozen alternate fields at which to land—all in case of a major malfunction.

Three pilots worked together as a crew for the first flight. They were Heimerdinger, a pilot for twenty-four years; William Magruder, formerly a test engineer for the United States Air Force

Flight Test Division; and Paul H. Patten, a test pilot for six years with extensive experience in the DC-6 and -7.

Before flying the DC-8, this veteran crew had spent thirty-five hours in the first flight simulator built for the big plane. Heimerdinger remarked that it was the "first time any crew has had the benefit of developing teamwork in a new airplane before making a first flight." The ballast on the original take-off included 6,000 pounds of demineralized water for injection in the engines to augment thrust. With Heimerdinger at the controls, the Eight was taken up to only 21,000 feet and to a speed of only about 350 miles per hour on the "easy-does-it" theory.

Perhaps some of the watchers on the ground remembered the story about a competing jet airliner that had been about to take off from New York. The pilot switched on his public-address system and said: "Good morning, ladies and gentlemen! This is your pilot speaking. I would like to welcome you aboard Flight 707, bound for Los Angeles. We will be cruising at an altitude of 34,000 feet, and the weather will be clear and smooth. We have a fine steak dinner prepared for you, with cocktails." At this point the invisible pilot, thinking he had switched off the loud-speaker, turned to his copilot. He commented softly: "We can give them all that guff, Frank, if I can just get this big fat monster into the air."

3

Nine DC-8's off the production line were designated to be tested in various ways from June, 1958, to June, 1960. This original schedule was greatly accelerated owing to the competition of Boeing and the 707. The first model was given preliminary evaluation and tested for flutter. There followed altimeter tests and stability and control check-outs. The radio and fire-detector systems, air conditioning and emergency drag chutes were also tried out, as were the mechanical-control system and stability factors.

The second plane had its shakedown; its J-75 engines were checked, and it was tested for flutter, pitching, rejected take-off and landing, air speed and the performance of the slots. Other checks indicated by the results of the first model were gone over in the second.

An example of one of the tests undergone by these models was the "yarn-field." It consisted of "sowing" specified wing areas with hundreds of short tufts of yarn. These showed the local vibrations with the same ease that a wind over a wheat field shows the force and direction of the breeze.

The third model checked out the usual items plus a test of the flight-control system, the fuel system, and calibration and trim compensation. The fourth tested out the air conditioning and added to it a check-out of the anti-icing, de-icing, and actual icing of the surfaces. Cabin-sound and pressure-level methods were tested, as were those in the cockpit. The generator was checked, the operation of the waste system, the acoustics of the fuselage, and similar items.

After the shakedown of the fifth model, it was checked for loading, the operation of the hydraulic-brake system, and another J-75 evaluation. The sixth and seventh models, using the same engine—three of the first four models had used the J-57 engine—went through miscellaneous tests, to which were added the problems of sound and terminal operations such as taxiing and take-off. The eighth model, after the usual checks, was used to evaluate such items as heavyweight brakes and new cabin-pressure levels. The ninth checked out the powerful Rolls-Royce Conway engines. (According to Bert Foulds, chief test pilot for Douglas, the problem of testing is becoming acute in the United States. On the West Coast, for example, the five test areas around Los Angeles are rapidly being built up—with the exception of Number 2, the ocean over which the DC-8 was flown.)

On the first flight there was enough data acquired visually, by instrumentation, and by recorders to evaluate totally the original flight. This information, however, took literally months to be digested and diagnosed by computers and mathematicians on the ground. The flights continued. By June 11, the first DC-8 had logged seven hours of air time. The third successful flight on June 7 was for 2 hours and 40 minutes. By that time, the DC-8 had climbed to 31,000 feet and reached three quarters of its test cruising speed of 586 miles per hour.

4

One of the major problems in testing airplanes is discovering the existence of "flutter" and how it can be either avoided or dampened. Flutter is a phenomenon that is explained most easily by whipping a flag through the air. The flag flutters. If it is whipped hard enough, if the flag is long enough, the flutter will rip the flag to shreds.

This same oscillation is set up by the turbulence of the air over swiftly moving surfaces of a plane. If the air does not follow its natural flow, there is an uncontrolled cycle of increasing vibration. This will ultimately destroy the whole plane—much as the continued vibration of a high note will crack a glass of crystal.

Flutter must be tested throughout the plane structure from the lowest speed to the highest—from a standing start, to the stalling point of 100 miles per hour, up to just below the speed of sound. In order to induce flutter, artificial means must be used. The DC-8 employed wing-tip vanes. Their rate of flapping could be changed from the cockpit. As they were shifted from one speed to another, they set up oscillation throughout the structure from which the plane itself was expected to recover. A second method of producing this kind of special vibration was done by firing shotgun shells imbedded in the wings. The sharp recoil induced a nasty jar. "We've got to shake up the DC-8 physically in order to find out where any danger points may be," said Foulds.

Every major part of every plane was checked in detail and in entirety before it was delivered to an airline. This included engine, tail, wing, fuselage, and so on. "We want the best and most complete information and the most honest estimates we can get on performance," said Foulds. "We made no major changes on the

DC-8, but almost everything was either changed or adjusted on the plane before it was checked out and went into service."

In order to make these check-outs, Douglas has sixteen engineering pilots and thirty others divided into production pilots for the off-the-line checks and reserve pilots who flew the smaller planes. As an illustration of how difficult it is to check out a single item, Foulds cited the fact that in most cases it took over half an hour merely to make an accurate estimate of how fast the airplane was going: "There are so many factors ganging up on you, such as fuel consumption, engine temperatures, level flying, condition of the air, altitude—it forms a very complex picture." The engineer-pilots had instruments that took pictures and recorders that played back the sound. As an additional precaution, they also took their own jotted readings of 120 instruments.

The airplane was also tested for such things as its performance in the maximum cross wind at landing. The selection of a runway for a jet airplane is quite important. "If we landed the DC-8 with a thirty-mile-per-hour tail wind," said Foulds jokingly, "we would need a runway as long as from Long Beach to March Field"— about fifty miles.

Nor was this the end of the testing department's work. Other pilots were assigned at home and abroad to the airlines—two men working forty-five days—to teach the characteristics of the DC-8 to the commercial pilots. It is an interesting sidelight that none of the test pilots spoke any other language but English. "English is enough," said Foulds. "You can come in for a landing in any part of the world, and the control tower will answer you in English."

5

As the tests took the DC-8 higher and faster, a new world surrounded the pilots. Taking off, the DC-8—unlike the big-thrust piston engines—started slowly without a surge of power. The gradual acceleration until take-off speed jangled some nerves. Rising upward toward 40,000 feet, both the earth and sky took on a new aspect. The sky shaded off from the blue into brilliant black, and the sun appeared brighter and smaller. The earth colors faded to drab. On clear days the horizon of the earth appeared clear. At such altitude the air was so free of foreign particles that it actually reduced cabin and cockpit illumination because of the lack of reflecting material. The pilots noted that more lighting for floor and corner areas was needed.

The cockpit had a system of red floodlighting for background depth perception and as an emergency service in the event of lighting failure. High-intensity flood lighting was provided to decrease the outside-inside brightness contrast during high-altitude daylight flights and during thunderstorms at night. The instrument panel had a master warning, fire warning, and master caution lights arranged at the center, to go on when any warning light showed outside the pilot's normal vision.

Cruising at about eight miles above the earth's surface, the radius of viewing rose from 174 miles (at 20,000 feet) to more than 246 miles with the DC-8 as the center. The bane of travelers, the unpredictable "holes in the air" that lift or drop a plane thousands of feet within minutes, was materially reduced. Ninety per cent of the gust-frequency bumpiness was eliminated when cruising went up to 20,000 feet; now 75 per cent of the remaining 10 per cent seemed to disappear. The ride became smooth and so silent ahead of the engines that mild thunderclaps could be heard in the storm-clouds.

Outside, when the DC-8 got up to fast speeds, the once-feared sound barrier appeared to the naked eye. It could be seen on the leading edges of the wings, a thin, wavering gray line that changed as one looked and as the plane moved. It seemed like an apparition of speed, a ghost of Mach. In the opinion of designer Wood, the DC-8 could very probably go over 760 miles per hour, although it might shake up the structure considerably. "As a matter of fact," said Wood, "we have had the Eight up to Mach .98, just under the barrier. We found that the buffeting and turbulence calmed down considerably at .92." The DC-8 can cruise at about Mach .88.

6

In the original flight tests, nine 80-foot water-filled tanks, 50 inches in diameter, were bolted in the middle of the plane. They weighed 45,000 pounds. Ninety gallons per minute were transferred between the aft and forward tanks, shifting the center of gravity rapidly, to test stability in flight.

Another test concerned a "trailing bomb." This dealt with the difficult air-speed determination spoken of by Foulds. It consisted of a 15-inch steel cylinder, 2 inches in diameter attached to a rubber hose 120 feet long. Trailing in the undisturbed air behind the DC-8, it calibrated speeds below 250 miles per hour. For speeds over 250 miles per hour, the speed was checked by low, level passes over special towers at Edwards Air Force Base or over a special Pacific Ocean speed course. From these air speed was calculated by wind direction and velocity, temperature, and air pressure—plus the time required to cover a measured distance and the plane's indicated air speed. The DC-8 was also paced by a smaller jet with instruments that had been previously adjusted. At high altitudes a kind of surveying telescope was also used to track the test DC-8.

In the air, as the "flutter" was set up artificially in the wings and tail, these vibrations were transmitted to ground stations by electronic telemeters and registered on visual charts like those used to detect earthquakes. Eight black lines traced continually at this land station gave the responses of the wings, control surfaces, nacelles, and other vital structural points. These were checked during flight and compared afterward. The old method was to use oscillograph recordings made in the plane, landing the test vehicle after every trip to look over the results. The new "constant monitor system" guaranteed results and allowed the tests to continue with the pilot receiving instructions by radio from the ground. The DC-8 flight testing thus safely explored conditions far beyond those to which the plane would be subjected in commercial service. Telemeters were also used to record engine temperature, the flow of fuel, speed, altitude, and similar items. (Douglas is steadily advancing toward the point where *all* data of test flying will be automatically telemetered, recorded, instantly checked and compared, with resultant safety and speed.)

A third test was centered on static stability—the tendency of an airplane in equilibrium, if disturbed, to return to its original condition. Another was stalling characteristics—the tendency of a nose-up plane to drop off. On the DC-8 a "stick shaker" is installed to vibrate the pilot's steering column as a warning. In the oscillation of the DC-8 the period of the vibration is about six seconds, and it takes less than thirty seconds to dampen it. Added to this, the DC-8 showed straightforward stall characteristics that were very similar to the highly respected, straight-wing DC-6 design. Good control was reported on all tests up to and through the stall in midair.

Once in a million miles of flight, an aircraft will receive a gust of 50 feet per second at heights of up to 20,000 feet. The DC-8 was tested to meet a truly rough gust of 66 feet per second, much as might be expected in the most severe thunderstorm. For emergency purposes the airplane was tried out in landings at maximum take-off gross weight. Directional control of the plane, maintained by the rudder, was checked to be effective at about 60 miles per hour. It was discovered that the DC-8 could bank three degrees either way before striking an engine pod on the ground. This was roughly the same clearance as the propeller of a piston-engine transport.

Owing to the refinement at the wing root, the DC-8 lacked the pitching characteristics that more sharply swept-back transport planes possessed. It seemed clear that the stability and control characteristics of the DC-8 were virtually as good as those of the classic DC-3. Even if hydraulic power failed and manual strength had to be used, the control forces on a DC-8 were only roughly equal to those on a DC-4.

7

To test the DC-8 de-icing equipment (it is possible to have two-inch hailstones in a storm at 35,000), special tests were made over periods much longer than could possibly be encountered in normal operations. During one such flight the plane flew on instruments in heavy icing weather for an hour and forty minutes. The ice-indicator drum showed 143 icing encounters. At one time there was a buildup of over two inches of ice.

With the de-icing system operating, the airplane remained clear of ice, with no refreezing of moisture. When the ice was allowed to accumulate, it was removed by one de-icing cycle. The ice on the engines was removed within five seconds in one test. Other ice on the windshield was removed in much the same time period. During these tests the expected hailstones were encountered without damage being done to the plane. Flying into and through thunderheads, the DC-8 was found to respond well in handling and absorbing the turbulence. At one point in the tests for de-icing, the pilot could find a sufficient amount of bad weather only over Fairbanks, Alaska. The plane was flown up simply to collect some specimens.

The inlets of the DC-8 engines were designed so they contained no mechanisms requiring extensive repairs or adjustment. This virtually eliminated the possibility of small parts and tools being forgotten where they might be drawn into the engine and ruin it.

On the ground, the Douglas-patented "blowaway" jet on the jet engines, which kept foreign material from being sucked into the intake, proved its value. In thousands of hours of test and operational flying, Douglas had not a single incident. Nor had eighteen Air Force bombers, with the same device, in two thousand hours. Five other bombers incurred major engine damage in the same period without the "blowaway." (Two such engine disablements were reported by one airline in the same period.)

As for the original landing gear that the pilots described as "kiddie kar" or "baby carriage" because of its ease of operation—turning 149 degrees of a circle—it had its difficulties. In January,

1960, with eighty-eight passengers aboard, a DC-8 made an emergency stop in Denver when a leak of hydraulic fluid developed. The plane came down and blew out all eight tires. The passengers emerged by sliding down the canvas emergency-exit chutes.

8

"I remember the old days," Douglas used to say. "Five hours in the open cockpit was all you could stand, because of the vibration and the noise." He was determined that the DC-8 would be better in this department. He realized that, as late as the DC-7, there had been serious complaints about the clots of air, the pressure roar that the propellers flung against the fuselage. He had not been able to promise Rickenbacker what he wanted, despite the fact that he had spent millions trying to figure it out. But the eventual level of sound in the cabin of the DC-8—even in the very sensitive areas behind the jet engines—did finally drop well below the DC-7 levels.

In the noise-suppression project the original goals of Douglas were reducing the noise at least from 9 to 12 decibels and getting the equivalent of at least 40 per cent of full power in reverse thrust at the same time. The reason for the noise in a jet take-off—the critical point in sound, since cruising is largely silent at high speeds —is the simple fact that hot high-speed gases expelled by the jet do not mix smoothly with cool outside air. The famous "daisy petals" and the retractable ejector finally tested by Douglas speed up this process and do not make the engine lose too much power. The ejector alone knocked down the sound four decibels and actually increased take-off thrust.

The relativity of sound has often exasperated engineers. It appears that the human value judgment of sound makes it either bearable or unbearable. An example: the lover of classical music may thoroughly enjoy a concert-hall crescendo that rises to 95 decibels. That same night in bed, the 25-decibel dripping of a leaky faucet may drive him out of his mind. The test pilots used this knowledge to fool an expert acoustic group.

The acoustic team, trying to discover the amount of noise at take-off, approached a Douglas check-out pilot and told him their duties.

"Where are you going to take the reading?" demanded the pilot.

"Down there," they said, pointing to the end of a long runway where their recorders were set up. The pilot nodded. They returned to their post, and he to his DC-8. He took off at full thrust, as straight up as he dared, leveled off, and crossed the invisible test barrier.

When he landed, the acoustic team was ecstatic. "That was the quietest jet transport we ever recorded," they cried. "Why, the decibel level was lower than a two-engine piston plane! You've got some new kind of noise suppressor, haven't you?"

The pilot shamefacedly confessed that he had. He had taken advantage of the DC-8 wing configuration, which allows control even at low speeds and altitudes. He had simply throttled back his engines, just before he crossed the check point.

9

By 1959, the three years of manufacturers' sales competition had turned into airline operations. The DC-8 was eight months behind the 707 in getting into the air. Passengers liked the latter fine—as demonstrated by the fact that they kept it 90 per cent filled. It was up to items like the Douglas seat (one expert prophesied it would be standard on all planes in five years), the size and flexibility, and the economic abilities to win the final point.

In the spring of that year, the jet pace quickened. The market was defined: re-equipping the airlines of the United States with such aircraft represented about $3,000,000,000 for 480 planes, plus their supporting equipment, maintenance, and terminal facilities. The foreign market, as well, suddenly seemed to burgeon. About the same time, in May, Douglas commenced building its fiftieth DC-8.

The testing program became so intensive that the FAA certification was granted one month ahead of the target date of October 1, 1959. General Clarence Irvine, one of the best-known flying generals of the Air Force, personally took up two models of the Eight. He reported: "It's the most stable airplane I've ever flown." Before the end of the next month, three international airlines and one domestic carrier had re-ordered twenty-one of the transports. At the same time the plane became part of the world's stamp collections: its image appeared on the 12- and 30-cent Netherlands stamps.

On December 1, United reported that the Eight had logged more than 3,508 hours cross-country and had accounted for a huge 12 per cent of the airline's entire revenues—with only six of the planes in the air. The gross weight on these trips was between 15,000 and 30,000 pounds greater than that of any other type of jet carrier.

The fourth DC-8 off the line spent more than 290 hours aloft in 155 flights covering 100,000 miles. It was the first to fly at an altitude of 45,000 feet with pressurization and at 40,000 feet unpressurized.

The seventh, called the "Young Airline" by the pilots, flew another 100,000 miles in six weeks and made 35 functional and reliability flights as well as 130 take-offs and landings at airports as far apart as Madrid and Montreal. It also established the first Eight speed record, flying from Long Beach to London in 10 hours and 42 minutes. Four months before, a Boeing 707 had flown an identical distance from Seattle to Rome in 11 hours and 6 minutes. This same Eight averaged 610 miles per hour in a flight from Los Angeles to Montreal. (The DC-8's mammoth appetite eats up enough fuel on a single trip to keep the average driver on the road for close to thirty years. It can cross the Atlantic between London and New York three times in less than fifteen hours.)

In March, 1960, the first DC-8 returned to its home base at Long Beach almost exactly two years after it took off for its first test. It had logged 311 hours and 227 flights. It had been brought home for rework and modernization, and to be equipped with new turbofan engines.

With its sister planes, it had made numerous expeditions to prove the worth of Douglas craft. DC-8's had landed at 8,240-foot altitude in Bogotá, Colombia. They had made an 8,715-mile trip through South America to prove their reliability over the jungle and mountains—in some spots taking off by using only 6,400 feet of a 10,000-foot runway. Over Mexico City, the Big Eight had come down from 42,000 to 14,000 feet in 47 seconds without any discomfort to a planeload of passengers—and had dumped 16,000 pounds of fuel in less than four minutes.

But the DC-8 had not entirely won the image of speed as well as it had trustworthiness in the popular eye. In March, 1959, the Eight had tried for a coast-to-coast transcontinental commercial speed mark. It made the trip in 4 hours and 13 minutes, 15 minutes slower than the Boeing 707. The public had not yet come to accept the DC-8 as it had the 707.

The cost-accounting figures showed what the desirable delay in making the better product had lost the company. In July, 1959, Douglas reported a net loss of nearly $11,000,000 in the second quarter of the year from DC-8 jet operations and boosted its prices on the big airliner from five to five and a half million dollars. In April, 1960, the loss for the preceding quarter was announced to run to nearly $7,000,000. This compared to a loss of a little over $8,000,000 for the three months before that. Research and development on the DC-8 had amounted to $6,250,000 for the former period.

The Big Eight was not yet making money. The company had delivered 44 of the planes out of 153 on order—plus about 20 more that were tentatively sold. Production of the DC-8 was up to eight a month. Military orders had taken over again—representing about 53 per cent of the $1,400,000,000 Douglas backlog.

FIFTEEN:

OF GIRLS AND MEN

1

THE LONG concrete strip with its laminations of black tire marks showed up clearly. The lights glowed along both sides. It rose slowly toward the plane, growing steadily nearer and nearer.

Suddenly the DC-8 developed a crazy yaw. It commenced to weave and buck. The runway bounced dizzily in front of the pilot. It jumped at him like an animal, hard concrete and the unforgiving ground.

The pilot wrestled madly with his controls. Nothing he did could bring the big plane back into line. It veered downward, one wing low. A crash was inevitable.

At the last minute, still staring horrified at what was ahead, the pilot gave an involuntary scream. He was helpless, doomed with his plane. The cockpit went black.

The lights went on and a door opened. "It was a hairy one, wasn't it?" inquired the instructor cheerfully. The pilot, recovering from his shock, replied fervently, "Don't ever put me through that again."

The instructor grinned. "How long do you plan to stay on the ground?" he inquired. The pilot managed to grin back at him. "Just

long enough to change one sweat-soaked shirt and some under-
wear," he said.

It was the finale of a simulator test. It had been held in one of
the $1,600,000 simulators of United Air Lines in Denver, designed
specifically to change piston-engine pilots physically and psychologically into semi-experienced jet pilots for the DC-8.

It costs nearly a thousand dollars an hour to fly the real DC-8.
It gulps fuel and, although the most manageable of the big jets, is
likely to take advantage of a pilot lapse. Although it actually has
fewer instruments, it needs new pilot habits. It is replacing one
kind of power with a radically different kind—and this at one
jump. To save expense, lives, and perhaps outright disaster, the
special training of the DC-8 pilots, like that in the military, must
turn to an uncanny imitation of the real thing.

2

The reason for the buildup of the strong simulator program for
jet transports, according to J. F. Martin, assistant director-flight
for Douglas, is that "habit patterns formed by pilots with twenty to
thirty years' seniority are not easily broken." In other countries
(such as the Netherlands with KLM), the top limit for the DC-8
captains is forty-six years; in the United States, an FAA regulation
requires pilots to retire at the age of sixty. If only a couple of
aspects of the problem of training are considered, it might be mentioned that the hourly cost of operating the simulator is one sixth
that of flying the plane, and that fifteen hours inside the fake cabin
will offer as much experience as a full year or more.

The original order for a DC-8 flight simulator—first of its kind for
an American commercial-transport jet—was sent out by Douglas
in April, 1956. The initial cost was more than a million dollars. It
called for a "total task-training device" that would provide a much
greater fidelity of simulation than ever before.

Douglas built a special installation to use the device. The object
was to train its own pilots as well as to provide preflight famil-

iarization to pilots of the airlines. Among the new features of the simulator were a motion system to create movements appropriate to the simulated maneuvers and accurate weather radar presentation. It was the first time a commercial device of this type got into operation before the airplane which it simulated got off the ground. Douglas put options on half a dozen more units.

By September, 1958, six airlines had ordered DC-8 simulators. It was estimated that a dozen hours of training in one of these machines would guarantee a smooth transition from piston-engine planes to jet commercial transports. Each simulator included all 120 instruments and controls used by the crew. The entire mechanism for such a simulator was housed in a building 15 by 15 by 90 feet.

The training program was set up to spend a week in preparing hypothetical flight plans and problem contingencies—such as not being assigned a requested altitude, or an unexpected temperature condition. A mythical loss of an engine or two was indicated to alter an original flight plan. Pilots were required again and again to recalculate fuel consumption and climbing procedures, vital sectors of any flight pattern.

Take-offs and landings were calculated with four- and three-engine take-offs; aborted ones were included. Four-, three-, and two-engine approaches, landing and go-around procedures were covered in the most realistic fashion.

The simulator training gradually became cumulative. The first day was a normal routine flight. Each day the program became more comprehensive, until the crew began to operate as a closely knit team. The last day in the simulator was a profile mission, taking off at a sea-level airport and landing at another one with an approximate elevation of 6,000 feet. Malfunctions were introduced on a basis of minimum fuel. The crew was called upon to make command decisions—such as whether they should return or continue. "The point of all this," said Martin, "is that there is only one right decision."

The so-called "trouble panel" was a console of switches and rheostats by which the instructor could imitate any emergency condition. A favorite emergency was training for the handling of engine fires. This kind of sweat-producing occurred a dozen times a day. One twenty-five-year piston-engine pilot, who had 25,000 hours of airline flying, including ten years over water, grumbled that he had three "fires" in twenty minutes in the simulator—three more than he had had in his entire career.

No examinations were given by Douglas, nor was any written record kept of a pilot's progress. Nor was any man's ability to fly the aircraft assessed. "We merely expose the individual to this training," said Martin. "What he gets out of it is up to him."

Douglas built two separate buildings on a thirty-nine-acre site for commercial jet training and publications. Other buildings have been designated to take care of the spare-parts provisioning and replenishment program which must keep the big airliners flying.

Symbolic of the continuing research going on is the ANIP "simplified control" question. Douglas has made operational an instrument panel that looks like a combination television set and organ console. Instead of 120 instruments, the pilot will be required to handle only a dozen. His major information will be gained from no more than three visual screens.

3

By April, 1960, nineteen airlines, including a large foreign contingent, were attending the DC-8 training program. Twenty-five different kinds of airline personnel were included in the eighty-two classes. The total number attending amounted to 2,533. At the same time, in the field, about 450 more airline personnel were being trained. Classes were being held in eighteen different locations—including Oslo, Norway, Lima, Peru, Tokyo, Stockholm, Copenhagen, Amsterdam, Paris, Rome, Buenos Aires, Spain, and Chile.

Before the piston to jet transition is over, the total cost will probably run to $250,000,000 for training alone. The advantage of the simulator over the real-life training in the plane itself is pointed up by the fact that the only fatal accidents involving pure-jet commercial transports have happened in training sessions.

The pilots themselves were worried about it. Said one twenty-year veteran: "Jets are such a big change-over that you wonder if you can make it."

In the spring of 1960, Pan American had finished training more than one hundred line crews consisting of captain, first officer, navigator, pilot, and flight engineer. This airline, unlike the Douglas preliminaries, gave regular tests. If the pilots were unsatisfactory, they were given additional training and retested. It was entirely possible for an old piston-engine pilot to be flunked. Captain William V. Moss, assistant in charge of pilot training for Pan American, said: "Pilots must get to the point where all old ideas are discarded and new ones become ingrained."

Pilots had to learn that jets simply do not give the same thrust as fast on take-off as the prop-plus-piston engine. They had to wait longer to get enough air speed. They had discovered they had to be very careful with the weaving "Dutch roll" effect and the tendency to flip over in a side slip. On landings the plane had to be brought in with nose low. If a pilot came in with a high nose, it resulted in a very hard and sometimes dangerous landing. A different type of throttle handling and a tendency to over-control had also to be checked.

The jet plane had to be flown precisely. Re-education was needed, a continued awareness, especially of fuel problems because of the fast rate of consumption. United flew a veteran check pilot with all newly trained jet captains for the first thirty hours. They got a recheck after one hundred miles of flight time. It will finish its own switch-over within the next two years.

The busiest DC-8 simulator in the United States is that run by United. It consists of a collection of instantaneous computers and closed-circuit TV screens. These are designed to co-ordinate to produce an exact replica of the flight of the DC-8 on the ground. Educating the three-man DC-8 crew in the intricacies of the cockpit costs roughly $25,000. (Pan American estimates are much higher.) Previous simulators for piston-engine ships, however, at United's own calculation, saved about $1,300,000 in six years. (A selling point of the simulator is that if the plane is delayed in delivery the crews may be trained regardless.)

About twenty hours of work in the simulator, plus twelve flying in the real transport, are estimated to be equal to more than one hundred hours of actual flight time. The result of such intensive training has been to eliminate a number of the older airline pilots. Many, over fifty years old, dropped the chance to switch to jets. Some abandoned the course in mid-term. One line flunked six of its first thirty pilots who received jet training. It appeared that the ultimate result would be younger and more adaptable crew members.

4

The DC-8 simulator is exactly what the name implies. It was built to exactly the same technical specifications as the real nose and cockpit of the airplane. The only difference was that it was a Fiberglas replica (unlike its predecessors), because of the weight problem of the original. Such a simulator did virtually everything the DC-8 could do—except fly. It reproduced, electronically, all aids to flight, navigation, instrument-landing system, and regular communication facilities. It showed the pretended fuel flow and pressure. Fuel in the simulator tank was consumed at the correct rate, changing the weight of the plane and shifting the center of gravity. Even the slosh of the fuel in the partly empty tanks was reproduced, as well as the squeak of the wheels on the runway and the bounce of the landing.

The electronic computers reproduced the power of the engines and the speed of flight. They also signaled the effect of air forces on control surfaces, rudder movement, buffeting, or braking. This was done by the lightning-quick action of the computer, which responded to the control signals and fed the action back as instrument readings, control field, vibration, noise, and acceleration.

With the use of a closed-circuit TV installation with movable camera, a map 10 feet wide and 70 feet long was scanned. This represented an airport and approach area 21,000 feet long and 3,000 feet wide. The "runway" itself was 12,000 feet long. The camera was synchronized so that it "flew" over the map in whatever position and altitude the simulator was reproducing.

This realistic presentation of the situation for the plane's cockpit was done by a fifteen-foot TV screen which gave a lifelike view of the airport on landing or take-off. The picture taken by a live television camera focused on a scale model in a neighboring room, representing a typical airport landscape. (Several of these were available to be used at various times.) The effect of the imitation was to associate flight and vision intimately so that the pilots and crews in training could add to the effectiveness of their education. This television was the work of a Douglas research engineer; combining it with the usual flight-simulator mechanisms made it possible to analyze the evaluation talents of the human pilot and the crew organization, something that before could be got only in actual flight testing.

Below the authentic replica of the DC-8 nose, hydraulic cylinders moved to simulate banking and turning, pitch and roll, climbing and descending, rough air and buffeting, even vertical acceleration. Computers were geared to a separate control circuit in the flight deck.

In "flying" the simulator, the crew had to figure payload weights, gross weights, cruise altitudes, climb angles, and other items of theoretical operation. These were changed to conform to variations in temperatures and conditions of wind and weather, from arctic cyclones to desert sandstorms. All of this was checked out by an instructor watching a computer in a console behind the pilots. There was a dummy traffic-control center with which radio contact was maintained. Instruments indicated changes in altitude, fuel load, and air speed. At the instructor's whim, even the visibility might be altered in seconds from noon brightness to night flight conditions.

Under emergency or abnormal weather conditions—produced by

the flip of a switch—the crew was expected to respond adequately. Rough air, failure of an engine, or breakdown of the hydraulic or electrical systems was authentically reproduced. The worth of the simulator was proved to Douglas when its own test pilots were given their thirty-five hours of indoctrination in this way before their first flight—and came through handsomely.

5

One airline buyer of DC-8's, Swissair, was worried about the time needed to service the Eight on the ground. It made a nine-man, three-month study of the problem. It was fined down to a necessary thirty minutes. "Unless we eliminate every wasted minute," the economical Swiss declared, "our planes will be expensive whales out of water."

Four fundamental rules were proposed: rigid passenger check-in times; mail and cargo ready to load; all personnel and equipment pre-positioned before arrival; strict discipline and co-ordination. A sample run-through was like this. Two minutes before plane arrival, thirteen items of equipment were manned and stationed. The necessary employees, including hostesses, were in readiness. In 2 minutes after the engines were shut down, the passenger stairs, electrical and pneumatic ground power, and fuel truck were in position. A minute later the passengers began to unload. In 5 minutes the first baggage cart darted out from under the plane. At 10 minutes passengers were clear; the cabin was cleaned in five more minutes. Refueling ended at 24 minutes. The water and toilet service was completed as the passengers loaded. At 25 minutes all the necessary food was aboard; at 28, the stairs were removed and the pilot started his engines. At 30 minutes the DC-8 moved down the runway, and those on the ground sighed in relief.

In routine flights—United has invested more than $30,000,000 in its DC-8 Hawaiian route alone—the big plane commenced to show its versatile reliability. With 35 per cent more seating and flights twice as fast, the airline got 70 per cent more real capacity.

Added wing slots cut 1,000 feet off the take-off runway length. In February, 1960, the DC-8 flew over 4,330 miles from Honolulu (at 68 degrees) to Chicago (snow-covered, at 16 degrees) in less than eight hours for a new civilian record—flying at 40,000 feet and nudging 600 miles per hour.

Occasionally there were failures of equipment. The outer panel of the cockpit windshield showed a tendency to delaminate under temperature changes. Once in a while the clamlike noise suppressors behind the engines failed to retract. But the virtues appeared to far outweigh the small defects. Pulled into a stall, the DC-8 recovered in a couple of hundred feet; it showed no tendency to slip off into a spin as did other big swept-back-wing planes. The turns in the sky never steepened or mushed out. Even the famous buffeting, the instability in lift caused by high altitude and high speed, gave it no more than a passing rumble, like passing rapidly over railroad ties.

Not all the pilots had been warned about the new conditions under which they flew the DC-8. One crew, flying in the first twenty minutes of their first flight, worked the adrenalin out of their system and commenced to relax. As they did, they heard a slight drumming noise. It commenced to grow. They sat up rigid in alarm, looking at each other. The ominous noise grew and grew; the throb seemed to shake the plane. The image of the feared, uncontrollable "flutter" shot through their minds. "What *is* that?" cried the captain.

As soon as he spoke, he knew what it was. The very fact that the others could hear him indicated what it was. He looked out of the cockpit window. He saw another plane—a propeller job—no more than a wing length away, taking publicity pictures. What they had felt and heard in the DC-8 was actually the noises of the piston engines next door.

6

Occasionally the gimmicks that were used during the tests—such as the drag chute—failed in their moment of glory. The pilots would rather have them fail than hesitate—as happened in one instance. Using the drag chute on a test plane, the pilot in command started his countdown audibly over the air so that a chase plane could photograph the operation of the chute. "Zero," he said, and pressed the button. Nothing happened. Everyone in the crew instinctively looked over his shoulder toward the rear of the plane. At that moment the malfunction corrected itself; the big 32-foot chute snapped loose. The jerk nearly decapitated all of the unready. They were massaging their necks for weeks. As for the photographers in the chase plane, the hesitation waltz in the sky was enough to lose them every one of their pictures since they had not expected the sudden flowering of the chute. "Incidentally," said a pilot, "letting that chute out is just like having God's own hand grab you by the tail up there. No other sensation like it in flying. And when you cut the chute loose, the Eight just glides away from it, as if you were sliding on a sheet of ice."

In the training, the crews were held together by the veteran Douglas pilots. Sometimes they had a hard time on their own. "If something really goes wrong to that six million in the sky," said one, "I wouldn't hesitate a minute about leaving it."

7

One of the roughest workouts (it was filmed for reshowing to the trainees) was that in which a DC-8 went full tilt down the runway, its nose as high as it could get, its tail six inches off the concrete. At about 150 miles an hour, the pilots *knew* the tail was that distance: a six-inch "tickler" was attached to it and when it struck the concrete it lit a bulb in the cockpit. It was the pilot's duty to keep the nose up, bump along, keep the light lit, keep full throttle, and keep the plane in balance. It was a fearsome thing to watch:

tires burning out, the landing gear exploding, the brakes squealing and smoking in agony. But it was faithfully executed to show the ruggedness of the landing gear and the stability of the Eight.

The crew took as much pride in training outsiders as they did in working on the test planes. Occasionally their patience with what they thought were the "whims" of the visiting pilots came to an end. One Dutchman wanted a special clock set into the instrument board. The production crew tried to get it and failed; temporized and was bawled out; and then was the victim of a collective dressing down. The next day the clock appeared on the instrument board. It was a small sand hourglass with a note: "Is this what you wanted?"

A few of the training pilots had their own superstitions. In doing "take-off rejection" work—where the DC-8 had to go up to full take-off speed and then be stopped in a certain distance instead of taking to the air—Heimerdinger wore a pair of shoes that were so old, ragged, and worn that about a third of his socks showed. He considered them good luck. So did the crew. They always solicitously inquired: "Are you adequately clad, Heimie?"

Another pilot always wore an old baseball cap on his head that dated roughly to the Black Sox scandals of the early 1900's. A third merely took a rabbit's foot. The training pilot explained the use of these fetishes by pointing out that "a new pilot, no matter how good he is, can make you sweat. You can't reach over and do his job for him. At a certain point in his training, if he's going to learn, you've got to sit back and close your eyes, and try to relax and pray at the same time."

In most cases the pilots liked the press, but they had to train their students for the inevitable questions. "What they always ask is always the same," confessed Heimerdinger. "We know them all: what's the speed, where are we now, what's the weight, and isn't this an easy job? And one more: why the hell isn't the lavatory working?" He recalled once, when he was sweating out a landing with a 200-foot ceiling around Baltimore and just managed to glimpse it, sideslip down, and land safely, a photographer rushed up. "What's the matter with you?" he shouted angrily, as Heimerdinger wiped his forehead. "You ruined my picture!"

8

The notorious "Easter egg hunt" of the Douglas training program forced the maintenance student to familiarize himself with 560 key points of the airframe and engine of the DC-8. Animated cartoons were used in classroom study, as were scale operating models. The course covered six weeks, divided into three sections: a two-week general course, another two weeks on airframe and power plant, a final two weeks on electrical and electronic detail.

This was only part of the three-pronged program given on DC-8 flight. Added to this Maintenance Familiarization were the other two phases: Flight Crew Familiarization and Field Familiarization. The second was mostly work in operations and emergencies in the simulator; the third was divided into maintenance and flight sections. All of them took weeks, running into months, to complete. Not before that were the men qualified, in the estimation of Douglas, to take over any key positions in the business of flying the Eight.

The DC-8 had about 5,000 visitors from sixty countries in the Long Beach division during its period of construction—all of whom seemed bent on familiarizing themselves with the huge plane. Most of them were either technical personnel or personages from various countries who came to make up their minds about not only the DC-8 but also the program of indoctrination.

In 1959, they included 2,032 from the United States, 174 from Japan, 99 from Sweden, 45 from Switzerland, 40 from England, 38 from Italy, 33 from Mexico, 27 from France, 25 from Spain, and 21 from Ethiopia. Australia sent 20, Brazil 18, while Holland, Denmark, and Turkey had 54, Germany 11. Russia sent over eight, including the famed designer Tupolev. Douglas obtained State Department approval of the Russian visit. It was noted that Tupolev was delighted by the Douglas patented landing gear and, it was sourly observed, "we can expect to see it turn up on a Russian transport any day now."

Ceylon (4), Canada (8), Colombia, Norway, Portugal (3), Paraguay (6), Pakistan (9), South Africa (2), Iran (7), Argentina, Cuba, Chile (7), San Salvador, Nicaragua, Venezuela, British Guiana, Costa Rica (10), Belgium (3), Greece (2), Peru (5), Indonesia, and Yugoslavia, all turned up at the factory. Other exotic visitors who indicated the span of the Douglas fame, especially in the Far East where any airplane is known as a "Dooglas-Dooglas," were Arabia (2), Korea (3), Morocco (3), Burma, Belgian Congo (2), and North Borneo.

9

These groups of foreign pilots and technicians formed a unique colony around the Douglas plants in Long Beach and Santa Monica. Since not all of them spoke English, they were remarkably shy. This fact was pounced upon by the unmarried Douglas female employees with great interest.

Parties were set up on the spur of the moment. At one of them, too many invitations were issued for a private home to accommodate everyone. One executive volunteered the use of a three-room office building he owned. Another managed to scrounge up four dozen chairs. One of the girls provided travel posters and pictures of planes; several others volunteered to decorate. Refreshments were provided on an everyone-bring-something basis. Most showed up with whatever they preferred to drink, plus a light snack. One man provided a stereo tape machine to furnish music for dancing.

The results of this impromptu hands-across-the-sea session were noteworthy enough to commend itself unofficially to Douglas. In the future, such parties—and all who were participants in the first series—may become the unofficial, informal hosts of the visitors from overseas. Douglas approves at least of the good intentions of the hosts.

"Flying planes can be either a warm international gesture," said one executive, "or it can be a cold-blooded, mechanical thing. We're past national boundaries now; we've gone into space before we've realized that aircraft have built up a whole new world of international relationships. We have to make our intentions as durable as a DC-3."

SIXTEEN :

IN THE DEEP HEAVENS

1

BY ALL that is holy in commerce, in those wheels of life that man turns so arduously only to be disappointed in the end, the story of the DC-8 is a romance.

It is another of those magnificent endings to an era. It is the day that comes to a close when another is born. Like the clipper ships of the days of Donald McKay, the days of the *Flying Cloud* and her white full-bosomed sisters, the history of the DC-8 is a climax that could have its fulfilment only in America. Even the time element has a curious parallelism: the first clipper, the *Ann McKim,* in 1832, the first DC-1 in 1932, a century later. The last of the great clippers of the East in the 1860's, the last of the great airplanes from the West in the 1960's, a century later.

The tale is the same. The famous races for supremacy on the sea and in the air; the fight against time and distance; the appearance of this wholly American phenomenon in the far places of the world —both have the same unmistakable, ineradicable trade-mark of glory that belongs to such tools of trade.

A romance it is, whether of a man with his creation or of the creature with the elements. The same charm of inspiration and of slow, integral development, of craftsmanship and service, of rivalry

and loss and gain. As the last of the clipper ships marked the passing of a legend on the seas, so the last of the great planes, the
DC-8, marks the passing of the conquest of the air. The sky may
be won again but not in this fashion.

These planes were the work literally of men's hands, busy about
the thousand tasks—whether the tiny rivets of the DC-8 or the
belaying pins of the sailing ship. Both tested the minds and ingenuity of their makers, no less than they brought out the iron
in those that flew or sailed. Built to serve what were the most common needs of man—to take him and his belongings from one place
to another—they found a special beauty of their own. If the prow
of the *Lightning* shearing the waves was a marvel to the sight, the
clean thrust of the DC-8 through the clouds was as wonderful to
another generation, no less approving and grateful.

"We always look ahead and try to do what has never been done
before," says Shogran with unconscious pride. "Sometimes we find
out that we have not been wrong." Writes Douglas on a photo to
a friend: "A dream come true that you helped accomplish."

That is the decent, humble credo of the men who worked for the
restless, impatient hearts of the travelers across the surface of the
only world they know; of the men who will work again for the same
travelers to visit worlds they will never know.

Those who create art in the service of the workaday goings are
different from those artists who bring it into being out of a secret
communing with themselves. Different but no less great in their
own right, perhaps greater in the multitude of hands that are always
lifting themselves upward with an aspiration of common pride. It
is no mistake that an aerodynamic creature is beautiful; it is all the
more remarkable that it is one of the most utilitarian objects of our
time. Perhaps it is no accident that, even before a plane maker,
Douglas was a sailor.

2

Now that the cycle of travel from here to there has come full
about, it may be understood that there is no end to it. In the new

field of progress, where man rises once more to a dimly known destiny, the DC-8 becomes only part of the pattern of progress. What it has contributed becomes part of the stock, blood, and bone of the advance into the unknown. From the days of William Christmas, the third American to fly a plane and who developed the 1918 "Bullet"—the first strutless, wireless, single-wing craft—to the days of the DC-8 is only a man's active life span (Christmas himself died in the spring of 1960). But the reputation of Douglas speaks loudly in the silences of aviation history. Witness the statement of Roger Rowe, speaking for Pan American–Grace Airways:

"Panagra has been a purchaser and user of every series of Douglas DC transport aircraft with the exception of the DC-5, and since 1938 we have operated nothing but Douglas aircraft. I believe this in itself speaks most eloquently. . . ."

Tomás Delgado, chairman of the board for Iberia Air Lines, wrote:

"At this time, when air traffic is changing from propeller to jet, for the greater world-wide enjoyment of our civilization, it is deeply moving to consider the figure of Douglas, whose name covers the whole of air-traffic history.

"From the time of those first three planes, which flew around the world at the 50th parallel, to the universal plane 'Dakota' DC-3 —passing by the model DC-2, which won the London-Australia race—it can be said that there has not been a moment in the annals of plane traffic in which the name of Douglas has not figured.

"After the late world war, the Skymaster DC-4 was the plane which permitted economic autonomy in air traffic and let the public become accustomed to transatlantic trips.

"Then came the Douglas models DC-6 and DC-7—even more famous in the history of commercial aviation and considered the last word or, better, the final achievement of propeller-driven planes.

"This story and these feats assure us that the DC-8 will continue the story of its predecessors—that quality which we call in Spanish *breeding*—and will contribute to the well-being of the present generation, which will see materialize its greatest dream—

that of being carried from any place on earth to any other place in one day."

But times change, for better or worse, in the air as in other modes of transportation. In *Life on the Mississippi* Mark Twain pointed out that it took thirty years for steamboat transport to come of age, "and in less than thirty more it was dead." Keelboating used to carry goods and passengers down the river's forty-three hundred miles in months. Steam took care of the two thousand miles between St. Paul and New Orleans in less than a week—and was killed in turn by the railroads that did the same trip in two or three days.

It appears to the prophets of the air that another similar revolution in transport is now in the making: now, when the 2,500 airmiles between Los Angeles and New York can be covered in four and a half hours. Unlike the other transportation systems, the airlines have concentrated on passengers. They look to the day when they can cut their air-cargo rates to a point where railroads and trucks will be outmoded competitors.

Beyond that point lies a wonderland full of conjecture and speculation. Some of it is educated on hard facts and experience. The rest of it is a tangle of wishes and hopes and expectations. They must feed on not much more than imagination. But, out of all the choices for the future, a few seem to be sure:

1. It will come at great cost. Unless there is a unique breakthrough in aeronautics, the astronomical cost of the supersonic airliners will keep them on the drawing boards. A break-through is certainly possible. Ten years ago, paying five and six million dollars for a single airplane was incredible. Aerospace developments have not yet had their chance to exhibit the developments of this wholly new science.

2. It will arrive with a jump. It will not come with the painful mile-by-mile increase of the piston-engine planes. Nor will it be as small a jump as that from 365 miles in piston engines to 600 in jets. It may go to a figure as high as ten times the present altitude and speed.

3. It will, apparently, be a product of the world to come. If, in the future, the countries about the globe are as divided and un-co-operative as they are now, it is probable that the new era of aviation may never be seen. Unless agreements can be come to upon international rights to space travel, it is impossible to predict any real advance. The prototypes may be planned (and are, as a matter of fact, in preliminary design now), but they cannot be put into production. They will be restricted to vehicles that cannot fulfill their promise.

4. It will limit itself perhaps to no more than two or three aerospace carriers of a kind. Both cost and the unpredictable nature of the cargo and passenger loads will forbid the building of more. As a corollary, the more profitable and certain field will lie in the short-hop, highly efficient, economical air transportation. This is the hard, unimaginative outlook. It is restricted to earth alone. But there are planets and landing places other than this good ground.

3

Aero-transport men do not talk too much publicly about space travel. It is still largely in the domain of science fiction. Yet it is noticeable that most of the engineers in the business keep a file of science-fiction publications. "They have what we don't have," explains one Douglas engineer. "That's imagination. They have crazy ideas, sure; but some of them work. We let them think them up. Then we spend money experimenting to see if they work."

On October 11, 1958, Douglas felt it could claim a space pioneering first that was far from fiction. That early morning, on the second try, a modified Douglas Thor rocket sent a three-stage experimental missile—under Douglas direction—into space toward the moon. The "Pioneer" was the first manmade object ever known to escape the air's gravitational field. It took the first payload into space. It rose to 71,300 miles before it turned back and burned up in the earth's atmosphere.

It was a victory for the United States: first into outer space.

The flight established a record for the greatest altitude and greatest velocity ever achieved until then by a man-manufactured object. It managed to record the first high-altitude measurement of radiation and of the earth's magnetic field. It was used as the first radio-repeater station that could bounce messages from one point to another halfway around the world.

Since that time Douglas rockets have sent payloads literally millions of miles into space. Some are still traveling. There have been a host of records, and the Douglas-trained men are responsible for more than half of them.

Under such circumstances it is not too surprising to note that Douglas made its first preliminary-design proposal for a space ship, using Air Force cash, early in 1946. Since then, for the following fourteen years, this design has been refined and modified until it is almost unrecognizable. Power plants and the vehicle have been immensely improved. Most of this has come from the continuing research exemplified by the tens of thousands of rocket missiles manufactured by the company.

According to Johnson, the chief Douglas engineer for missiles and space systems, the space ships may very well base their final design on the general size and shape of the DC-8, altered only for the exigencies of space travel. He feels nuclear power will be used. It will give the space frame a boost up to 25,000 miles per hour, the speed necessary for escaping the earth's field of gravitic force. Johnson believes these aerospace DC-8 types will be used in the traditional sequence—first for military reconnaissance, surveillance, navigation, and communication. Finally they will be used for commercial travel and exploration.

According to M. W. Hunter, one of the top engineers for Douglas space systems, "The ultimate in our concept would be a single-stage spaceship made completely re-usable in the fashion of a normal aircraft. Actually, a DC-8 airframe is rather expensive but because its price is amortized over a large number of flights, the effect of its initial cost upon direct operating cost is negligible." Hunter continued his comparison by stating that lunar transports, for example, might "carry roughly half the payload of the DC-8" and that if a DC-8 applied a tenth of the weight of the airplane as energy for five hours, this amount in "field-free space" would be enough to carry it to the moon.

Johnson pointed out in an address to the Society of Automotive Engineers that the ballistic missiles of the present age—themselves being trans-space ships of one kind—will be used as basic research for the final product. "However," he added, "while ballistic missiles in the next few years must get smaller, space ships dependent upon chemical fuels must get much larger than anything yet built." Thus the commercial versions may run counter in development to the military because of the large amount of supplies and technicians required.

4

The attitude of the Douglases—junior and senior—toward the future is not always eye-to-eye. There is an undercurrent of disagreement which characteristically shows up in their conversation.

"We expect to dominate space travel, just as we have dominated atmospheric flight for the last twenty-five years," says the son. It is an aggressive statement. It is not altogether true even in its historical implications. On the other hand, the elder Douglas says: "I don't suppose we'll ever dominate aviation again the way we did with the DC-3, but we intend to have our full share."

Donald, Jr., recognized that the company his father founded when his son was a toddler delivered 53 per cent of the world total of airliners by the end of 1958, but this was by no means the only kind of "atmospheric flight" in vogue. He had gone through a half-dozen jobs in the sprawling billion-dollar company—in power plants, testing, and sales—and could be expected to know it thoroughly. He has emphasized that the diversification of the company is proceeding in high gear. In a report to the stockholders, he declared:

"The variety of our products remains great: from shipboard attack aircraft for the Navy to transports for the Air Force and the commercial market; from short-range Army field missiles to major space vehicles; from the world's most effective anti-aircraft missile to the world's only air-to-air nuclear rocket; from advanced concepts of anti-submarine warfare devices to the only anti-ICBM defense system under development anywhere; from conversion of older passenger transports to air freighters to research and development of the most advanced cargo aircraft in the world; from the study of nuclear-powered space travel to the development of an advanced cargo-handling system that will revolutionize not only the Air Force's transportation system but offer big dividends to private commerce as well."

The pride in the DC line and its reliability of performance has persisted well into the aerospace era. In the spring of 1960, young Douglas referred to the 85 per cent reliability of the Thor as "the DC-3 of the space age." He noted that all launches had been executed by company teams; and that Thors had put payloads into orbit near Venus, boosted a television satellite, and had hung "an artificial North Star," the world's first navigational satellite in space.

Young Douglas is advocating the next generation of air travel as a Mach 3 plane (about 2,300 miles per hour). His father, on the other hand, cocks a skeptical eye at the whole idea. He feels that a plane that can cross the continent in an hour and a half—built at tremendous cost—may not be worth the effort. "With a little more time and work," he says, "we can make missiles that will carry passengers from Los Angeles to New York in twenty minutes."

It is clear who is the young fogey in such circumstances. The father is still thinking ahead of the son, but he feels that Douglas, Jr., has the "know-how and the want-to." He is willing, if his son wins the arguments fairly, to go along with his ideas even to the point of getting out of the picture entirely.

He knows he has two other sons, William and James, coming up steadily through the ranks. They will be on hand to take over the arguments with the elder son. He expects to lean back on a beach and listen, without too much interest. But before he leaves his post as chairman of the board, the elder Douglas—patriarch of the plane-building clan—wants his company in better financial shape. The answer for the time being is not in reaching out and grabbing a handful of space, at least for the Old Man. It is in the good business principles that he knows where money can be made while simultaneously advancing his beloved aviation.

5

The attitude of Raymond toward the horizon is conservative. He looks on what is to come with the cold eye of a man who has seen a thousand experiments for a single success. He is gratified but not enthusiastic about it all.

"If we ever go into a supersonic plane," says Raymond, "it will be because there is a demand and it is economically possible. It means Douglas will have to abandon some of its cherished safety principles. For example, the fuel and the passengers will have to be intermixed, so to speak; the fuel will be in the fuselage. We have always tried to keep it in the wings; but in the supersonics the wings will be unable to carry it. Perhaps in the tail—but how much can you store there? The passengers will be literally on the inside or perhaps in the front end of a bomb."

He goes on to say that other changes will be necessary. "I don't know yet how we can get visibility on a supersonic," he says. "No windows will be possible, as far as we know, at that speed. How will the pilot see? If he can cruise by instrument, fine. Maybe the passenger psychology will have been advanced enough by that time to get them to crawl into a stainless-steel cave. Look what we do in windowless air-conditioned office buildings now."

Raymond also worries about the noise problems. "I don't know of any way to stop such a plane from being a general nuisance to the public," he says. "You have to consider take-off, cruising, and landing. If you think sonic booms are bad now, the launching of such a plane would be a daily catastrophe. Douglas, for instance, has spent about $30,000,000 to date on noise suppression. We think we have gone about as far as we can." Raymond points out that noise is almost always a concomitant of energy within the atmosphere. "If a plane is perfectly silent," he says wryly, "it is also perfectly motionless."

Raymond admits that his feelings are all predicated "on the present state of the art." He feels that future technological developments may make him a liar, that a break-through of major scientific proportions may reverse the whole picture. "But I can't see, given the limitations of existence as they are, how we can do it," he declares.

In this connection, other aerospace investigators—such as those of the Bell Aircraft company, whose founder worked with Douglas —have projected their ideas into the 1980-90 period. They predict rocket-powered transports boosted by a ramjet that will carry a piggy-back boost glider with passengers. The "mother transport" will rise to about 20 miles. Then the "child" will shoot itself up to 43 miles and finally glide down to its destination. The speed would be above 15,000 miles per hour, making a Los Angeles-to–Paris trip feasible in a little over that span.

These researchers believe that the development cost of this single idea would be approximately a billion dollars at the time of its growth. Even thirty passengers aboard at a time would make a flight profitable, riding in an air-conditioned womb, while outside the skin of the vehicle glows red-hot.

Ed Burton, as vice-president in charge of engineering for transport-aircraft systems who was instrumental in creating the DC-8, made a study of the time and labor involved in developing the later models of the DC series. He reported that 740,000 engineering man-hours were needed for the DC-6. For the DC-8 the figure was 6,600,000 man-hours. To design the specifications for the Mach 3 (or better) vehicle would require at least 15,000,000 man-hours of engineering. Regardless of the development cost, which would run into billions, a single Mach 3 airliner might run about $25,000,000 in airline costs.

Atomic power for propulsion exists in plenty. The amount of nuclear explosives in the United States, according to H. S. Aurand, of the technical military planners of General Electric, consists of a stockpile of about 5,000 megatons—equivalent to 5,000,000,000 tons of TNT in power. If all uranium available to this country from proved reserves of high-grade uranium were assembled, says Aurand, it would amount to roughly 2,000,000 tons, worth $80,000,000,000 at current prices. The total yield of energy of this —together with about 80,000 tons of obtainable lithium deuteride —would be about 40,000,000,000,000 tons of TNT. The power inherent in such a mass may be estimated by the fact that the strongest natural earthquake releases energy in the nature of only about 2,000,000 tons of TNT. The total annual energy of all earthquakes all over the world is about 30,000,000,000 tons of TNT. Aerospace will get the major benefit of such power magnitudes in the future.

6

Douglas is now running three separate programs trying to get the reported costs of the North American B-70 experimental military nickel-steel bomber down to about one tenth of its present $150,000,000 cost. "We think we can do it," says Wood. As far as the advances in aeronautics are concerned in a military sense, if a plane flies it can almost immediately be considered obsolescent. It usually wears out in about 2,000 hours of flying. In ten years Douglas expects to have a commercial plane that will fly at 3,000 miles per hour and last for ten times that period.

On the cargo-transport future, the prospects are even more visible to the non-crystal gazer. According to Ed Burton: "The company's concept is for an airplane that will operate at four cents a ton-mile direct costs, incorporating a complete mechanical loading system and a swing tail for rear loading." Burton notes that there have been tens of millions budgeted as of 1960 by the armed forces transportation services for planes with new and improved engines. He feels that there is a commercial potential of "several hundred airplanes during this decade." He adds: "A true cargo aircraft with present DC-8 ranges and speeds and a payload of over 100,000 pounds can be available in 1963."

Foulds believe that planes like the DC-8 will simply be enlarged and speeded up. Power plants of double the present thrust (or about 36,000 pounds apiece) are already on the scene. The fuselage designs to match are on the way. "Our big problem is noise," he says emphatically, "and where to land without taking off the top of someone's head." He points out that in many of the landing fields in the world, houses are built up right to the edge of the area. Foulds feels that there may eventually be "continental" airports. He means by that that there will be one airport for all of Europe, another in the middle of Africa or the United States, others in Asia and South America. He believes that vast descendants of the DC-8 will fly at great speeds to such central points without hazard to ground dwellers, disgorge their passengers, and get them transferred to smaller, feeder planes to take them to their various destinations. "Imagine an ocean liner putting in at Atlantic City and Fort Lauderdale and so on down the coast," he explains. "Ships and trains have got away from the little stops. So have buses, to a large extent. I think we'll come to it in the air."

7

Part of the only DC-1 that Douglas ever made still survives. It still "flies," although in a different sense than its designers intended. In a story attributed to Douglas himself, it was originally sold to TWA as part of the first batch of planes ordered by Frye. After five years in routine transport, it was sold to the famed designer and pilot, Howard Hughes. Hughes seriously considered it as his vehicle for his 1939 three-day round-the-world trip.

In 1935, Hughes sold it to Viscount Forbes, Earl of Granard, an amateur pilot who was planning a transatlantic speed dash. Forbes decided against the venture. He peddled the original DC-1 to a broker, who sold it to the Spanish Republican army air force. It served for years as a transport and reconnaissance plane.

Captured, the plane was repainted and redecorated as a Spanish airliner after the civil war's end. It became part of the Iberia Air Lines, flying over the Pyrenees mountains. In December, 1940, an engine failed in take-off. The heavily overladen plane came down at the end of the runway about one hundred miles from Barcelona. World War II prevented any serious attempts at salvage.

Nevertheless, it was discovered that part of the plane was still in existence, more carefully and reverently treated than at any time in her arduous life. The priests from the nearby town of Málaga picked up most of the fuselage. They made it into an *anda,* a primitive metal stretcher on which the image of Mary, the Blessed Virgin, could be carried through the town streets on *fiesta* days.

Just as the sole DC-1 still "flies" with its image of a passenger, so do most of the other Douglas planes. The DC-2's are still in use; the DC-3's seem imperishable. The DC-4's can be seen on many of the world's airways; the DC-6's and -7's are still long-distance economy work horses. No one can even estimate the number of people or the tons of cargo they have toted around the globe. The world-wide system of technicians and engineers who can be found in every civilized country—and in some not so civilized—may be the harbinger of the great union of aircraft ideas which must prevail if world commerce is to live. The precious bales will not drop from heaven of their own accord; there must be planning and experience and continuing conquest of what now lies outside man's knowledge and daring. From pistons to jets to ramjets in the upper air—and on to rockets and ion propulsion or a combination of them all—with the frames of the imigination to span space.

8

So, at long last, the vision that served the frontiersmen of aviation so well becomes clouded. They cannot see what will be or the choices that must be made. Perhaps it is best to leave it so, in their care.

It may be that the men who came up from baling wire and canvas to jets and monocoque are not the real prophets at all. Their sentiments are too much with the past: they see the image to come through the distorting lens of their own experience. New minds, new dreams are needed. If an airplane is to be no more than "a bunch of nuts and bolts flying in close formation," it is worthless anyway. What Douglas and the men who built Douglas must hand on to the survivors is the will to go on, no matter the cost.

The aircraft-manufacturing business is peculiar. It has, almost alone of all modern industries, remained a craftsman's paradise. In spite of the massive work done by assembly lines and machines, in the end any DC-8 is a product of loving care and the caresses of its hand tooling. It has remained, too, a business with remarkable standards of humanity and the vices and virtues of such a temperament. If Douglas has made mistakes in his labor relations, he has made none in his uncompromising faith in his profession.

A business that produced the DC-8 as its pinnacle has a right to survive. In the modern hurly-burly of efficiency, Douglas has not always indicated a corporate immortality. It has led a roller-coaster existence, up and down in sales and product, never surrendering its quality but sometimes sadly wanting in quantity. It has not diversified: it is still virtually entirely in the business of making aero-stuff. As such, it suffers with the fickle changes of the market. It thinks big because it deals big, but it has little cushion against the impact of general economics.

Perhaps this will change, perhaps not. Possibly the ancient and stubborn resistance of the men who created aviation as it stands astride the world today will not yield to the cost. Whether or not Douglas survives in the competition of the aerospace age, it is enough to have built one DC-8. It is a product that future generations will wonder over and admire in archaeological discovery—as the statuary of lost civilizations requires our own affection. More than any other single artifact, the DC-8 is the symbol of our time before its descendants plunge away from the world and toward a new destiny. It is the craft that has nearly left its second environment, something that has never occurred yet in evolution.

If the DC-8, in the nature of the aluminum-alloy beast, cannot, its children will. Heaven is no mistake. The trail of the emblem Douglas has had carved for so long in his personal desk—the human heart and wing—still leads upward.

INDEX